A *guide to* . . . .

. . . . *managing*

health and

safety in

construction

HSE BOOKS

© Crown copyright 1995
First published 1995
Applications for reproduction should be made to HMSO

ISBN 0 7176 0755 0

Contents

Contents

INTRODUCTION

1   Everyone working on a construction project has health and safety duties and responsibilities. This publication provides guidance on how to comply with the Construction (Design and Management) Regulations 1994[1] (CDM Regulations) throughout the various stages of a construction project. Detailed guidance for those involved in the design process is given in the Construction Industry Advisory Committee (CONIAC) publication *Designing for health and safety in construction*[2].

2   The CDM Regulations place new duties upon clients, designers and contractors and create a new duty holder - the planning supervisor. The Regulations also introduce new documents - health and safety plans and the health and safety file. All these duty holders have a role to ensure that health and safety is taken into account and managed effectively throughout all stages of a construction project. This may require many organisations to re-think their approach to health and safety. Those who already have appropriate procedures which integrate health and safety throughout the various stages of a construction project may find they already do what the Regulations require.

3   This guidance aims to help all duty holders under the CDM Regulations on any size of notifiable project (see paragraph 16). To help you understand your duties and be aware of the duties of others the guidance follows the construction process through five stages. The stages are highlighted below:

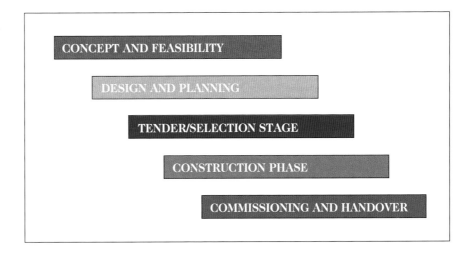

The guidance is structured in this way for clarity, however, it is evident that within certain forms of procurement (eg design and build or management contracting) there is much more of an overlap in the roles of the duty holders at the different stages of a project. Nevertheless the principles which are outlined at each stage in this guidance still need to be considered and integrated into project design, planning and execution by each of the relevant duty holders.

Introduction

4   Readers need to identify their own particular role such as client, planning supervisor, designer, principal contractor or contractor. They should ensure that they understand what they and others need to do under the CDM Regulations and discharge their responsibilities accordingly.

5   A new approach and commitment to health and safety is required by all those in the construction process who can contribute to the avoidance, reduction and management of health and safety risks. Each duty holder under the CDM Regulations has a different and clear role. By working together through teamwork and collaboration with other duty holders, all parties can improve health, safety and welfare standards on construction sites and for subsequent work (eg maintenance).

6   Various terms are used in this guidance and the glossary at the back of this publication provides an explanation of these. Reference is also made to specific CDM Regulations in the guidance and Appendix 6 provides a summary of where these apply to the duty holders at the different stages of a project.

7   In this guidance the five stages of a construction project referred to in paragraph 3 have been given working definitions and these cover the following activities:

Concept and feasibility: This stage begins when the client first thinks about having a structure built, repaired, refurbished, demolished or maintained. It overlaps with the start of detailed design work. During this period important decisions are made on layout and outline, overall scheme and initial design and construction methods.

Design and planning: During this stage detailed design work takes place. Final decisions on matters related to design and specification are made. Final production information (eg drawings) and specifications are produced. The preparation of information for the tendering process also begins. For some forms of procurement, there will be considerable overlap with actual construction starting.

Tender/selection stage: This stage primarily involves the selection of the principal contractor for the construction process. The final production of tender documentation (eg bills of quantity) and the procedures and processes for the selection of the principal contractor take place.

Construction phase: This stage covers the time for the principal contractor to plan, programme and prepare the construction work. Arrangements are made to start the work and then carry out and manage it.

Commissioning and handover: This stage includes the activities required to bring plant, equipment, building management and similar systems into operation and finally the structure is handed over to the client.

When do the CDM Regulations apply?

8　　The CDM Regulations apply to most building, civil engineering and engineering construction work including:

(a)　new-build construction;

(b)　alteration, maintenance and renovation of a structure;

(c)　site clearance;

(d)　demolition and dismantling of a structure;

(e)　temporary works.

9　　The CDM Regulations also apply to all design work carried out for construction. However, there is one exception to the above (please see paragraph 10).

When don't they apply?

10　The CDM Regulations do not apply to construction work when the local authority is the enforcing authority for health and safety purposes. This means that where work is not notifiable (see paragraph 16) and is:

(a)　carried out inside offices, shops and similar premises without interrupting the normal activities in the premises and without separating the construction activities from the other activities; or is

(b)　the maintenance or removal of insulation on pipes, boilers or other parts of heating or water systems;
it is not subject to the CDM Regulations.

11　The CDM Regulations also do not apply to construction work if:

(a)　the work will last for 30 days or less and involves four or less people on site at any one time; or

(b)　the work is carried out for a domestic client (someone who lives, or will live, in the premises where the work is carried out). In this case, only the duty to notify the Health and Safety Executive (HSE) applies. However, in some instances domestic clients may enter into an arrangement with a developer who carries on a trade, business or other activity. For example, a developer may sell domestic premises before the project is complete. The domestic client then owns the incomplete property, but the developer still arranges for the construction work to be carried out. In this case the CDM Regulations apply.

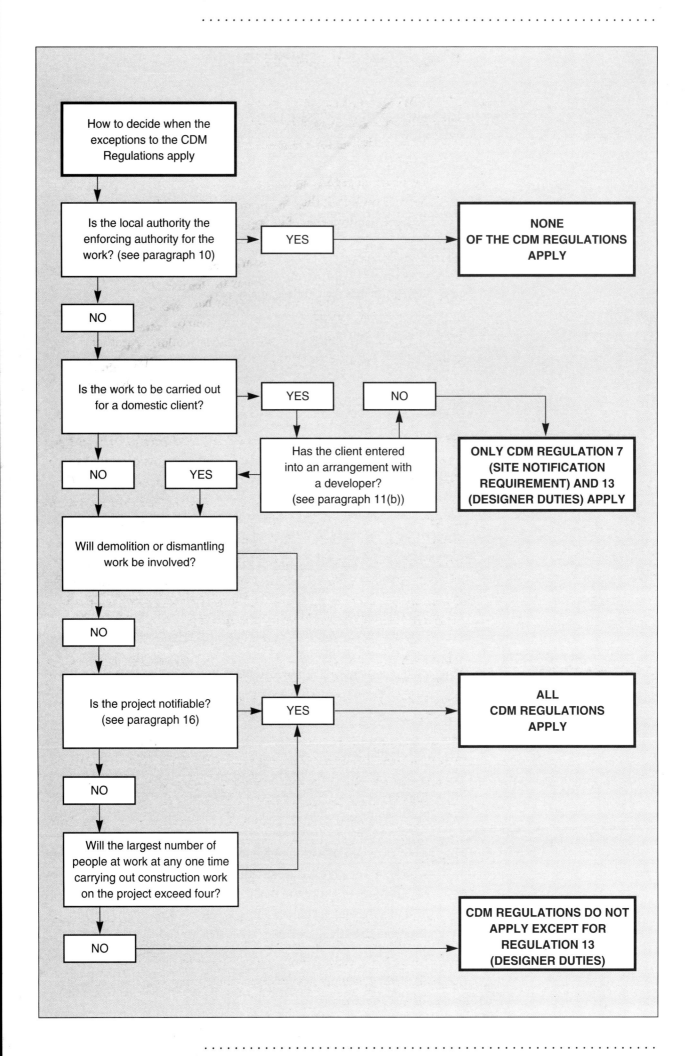

How to decide when the exceptions to the CDM Regulations apply

↓

Is the local authority the enforcing authority for the work? (see paragraph 10) → **YES** → **NONE OF THE CDM REGULATIONS APPLY**

↓

NO

↓

Is the work to be carried out for a domestic client? → **YES** → Has the client entered into an arrangement with a developer? (see paragraph 11(b)) → **NO** → **ONLY CDM REGULATION 7 (SITE NOTIFICATION REQUIREMENT) AND 13 (DESIGNER DUTIES) APPLY**

↓   ↑ **YES**

NO   **YES** ←

↓   ↓

Will demolition or dismantling work be involved?

↓

NO

↓

Is the project notifiable? (see paragraph 16) → **YES** → **ALL CDM REGULATIONS APPLY**

↓

NO

↓

Will the largest number of people at work at any one time carrying out construction work on the project exceed four?

↓

NO → **CDM REGULATIONS DO NOT APPLY EXCEPT FOR REGULATION 13 (DESIGNER DUTIES)**

Introduction

Demolition and dismantling

12   The CDM Regulations apply to all demolition or dismantling work except where the work is inspected by local authorities (see paragraph 10) or where it is carried out for a domestic client (see paragraph 11 (b)).

13   The flow chart on page 4 will help you to check if the CDM Regulations apply to your project. If they do, inspectors from HSE are responsible for enforcing the requirements of the CDM Regulations.

14   The CDM Regulations do not necessarily apply to contract arrangements such as fixed term contracts which may involve maintenance or emergency work on a frequent or irregular basis over a long period. However, the Regulations may apply to an item or section of work forming part of the contract. If many items or sections of work forming part of the contract fall within the application of the CDM Regulations, the client may find it useful to apply the principles of the Regulations to the contract as a whole.

Example

The client, a property owner, let a fixed term contract for maintenance of an office building to a contractor. As the items of work were carried out without interrupting the normal activities in the office, the local authority was the enforcing authority and the CDM Regulations did not apply. However, following some wind damage to the structure, the client required the contractor to carry out the repairs. It was anticipated that this work would take three months and so the CDM Regulations applied to it and HSE was the enforcing authority.

Example

The client, a local authority, put out to tender a two year fixed term contract for the maintenance of highways. Much of the work involved surface dressing, minor civil engineering works, kerb and paving repairs. Many of these items came within the CDM Regulations because they involved more than four people. The client decided to apply the requirements of the CDM Regulations to the whole of the fixed term contract rather than separate out the elements to which CDM applied. This made handling the contract much easier in logistical and practical terms.

15   When the CDM Regulations do not apply, the Health and Safety at Work etc Act 1974[3] (HSW Act), the Management of Health and Safety at Work Regulations 1992[4] (MHSW Regulations) and other health and safety legislation will still apply to employers, and the self-employed carrying out construction work.

Notification

16   If the construction work is expected to either:

_____

(a)   be longer than 30 days; or

_____

(b)   involve more than 500 person days of construction work;

_____

HSE has to be notified in writing. The flow diagram on this page will help you check if your project should be notified to HSE. There will be some cases when the CDM Regulations will apply to the work but the project does not need to be notified. For example, construction work which lasts 20 days and involves 10 people comes with the CDM Regulations but does not need to be notified. Further guidance on notification can be found in paragraphs 28 to 29.

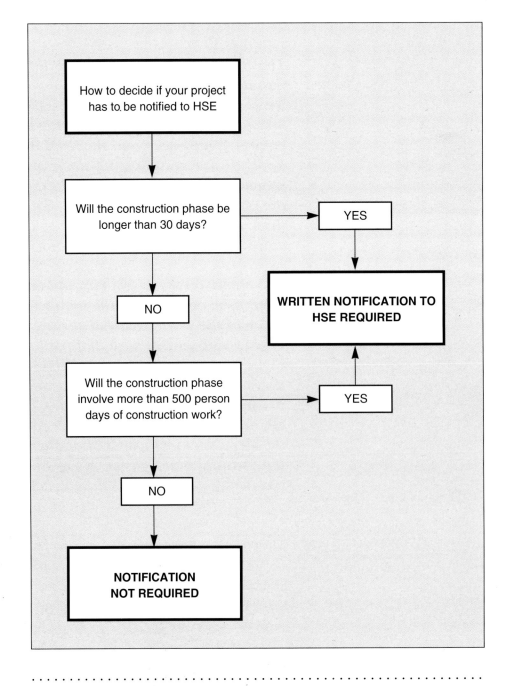

THE CONSTRUCTION PROJECT

Stage 1   CONCEPT AND FEASIBILITY

Stage 2   DESIGN AND PLANNING

Stage 3   TENDER/SELECTION STAGE

Stage 4   CONSTRUCTION PHASE

Stage 5   COMMISSIONING AND HANDOVER

STAGE 1: CONCEPT AND FEASIBILITY

17   A number of key tasks are carried out by or on behalf of the client during the concept and feasibility stage of a project. Fundamental decisions are made about the project which will affect health and safety during construction and subsequent work (eg maintenance and refurbishment). The CDM Regulations require that health and safety are addressed and co-ordinated from this very early stage.

THE CLIENT

The client's key tasks during the concept and feasibility stage:
■   determine if the project falls within the scope of the CDM Regulations
■   appoint a planning supervisor
■   be reasonably satisfied that the planning supervisor and any designer(s) who the client arranges to prepare a design are competent and have made adequate provision for health and safety
■   provide the planning supervisor and designers with information relevant to the health and safety of the project

Determine if the project falls within the scope of the CDM Regulations

18   At the very outset, the client needs to consider if the project will come within the scope of the CDM Regulations. The flow chart on page 4 will help you determine whether the CDM Regulations apply to the project. If they do, a planning supervisor will need to be appointed as soon as it is practicable (see paragraphs 22 to 24). However, before the planning supervisor is appointed, clients may wish to appoint an agent to act for them (CDM regulation 4(1)).

Appoint an agent

19   If the client appoints an agent, the latter is responsible for carrying out the duties of the CDM Regulations. Clients with limited knowledge of the procurement and construction process may find that appointing an agent is a useful way of ensuring the client's duties under the CDM Regulations are carried out. Also, if there are a number of clients involved in a project it may be useful to appoint one of them as the agent. This will allow a single organisation to take on the duties of the client and avoid any confusion over responsibilities for health and safety.

20   If an agent is to be appointed, the client or clients will need to be satisfied as well as they reasonably can that the agent is competent to carry out the duties. For further guidance on competence see Appendix 1. Appointing an agent with experience and knowledge of the design and construction process will help ensure that the duties of the client are carried out properly.

21   If a client or clients appoint an agent, a declaration has to be made to the local HSE office (CDM regulation 4). The declaration should be in writing and has to:

(a)   explain that the agent is acting on behalf of a client;

(b)   include the name of the person making the declaration;

(c)   contain the address of the person who is making the declaration;

(d)   contain the exact address of the site; and

(e)   be signed by or on behalf of the agent.

Appointing an agent does not mean that the client is relieved of duties under other health and safety legislation, eg HSW Act and MHSW Regulations.

Appoint a planning supervisor

22   The client has to appoint the planning supervisor as soon as possible so that the latter can from this early stage:

(a)   advise on the competence and the adequacy of provision for health and safety made by any designer who the client arranges to carry out design work;

(b)   ensure designers comply with their duties under the CDM Regulations;

(c)   co-ordinate health and safety.

23   The CDM Regulations allow flexibility when deciding who should be appointed planning supervisor. The role can be carried out by the client, the lead designer (eg a firm of consulting engineers, an architectural practice, etc), a contractor or an organisation working as specialist planning supervisors. The choice of which organisation is most appropriate to carry out this role is of critical importance and depends on a number of factors, including:

(a)   knowledge of the construction and design process;

(b)   the particular skills and expertise required for the project;

(c)   the prospective planning supervisor's management arrangements and procedures for carrying out the role of planning supervisor.

Make sure the planning supervisor and designers are competent and have provided for health and safety

24   The planning supervisor should be competent to carry out the job and should have made adequate provision for health and safety. In most cases the duties of the planning supervisor will be carried out by a team of people bringing different skills to the project (eg design and construction experience and, where appropriate, health and safety). Except for the smallest projects, it is unlikely this role will be carried out by an individual. Further guidance on competence and provision for health and safety can be found in Appendix 1.

25   Where a client arranges for a designer to prepare a design for the project, the client has to be satisfied as well as they reasonably can that the designer is competent and has made adequate provision for health and safety (CDM regulation 8(2) and 9(2)). The client may need to seek professional advice on whether the designer is competent and has made adequate provision for health and safety. The planning supervisor is under a legal duty to provide this advice if requested (CDM regulation 14(c)).

Example

The client for a large civil engineering project which involved a considerable amount of design and planning work by a firm of consulting engineers appointed them for the role of planning supervisor. The client considered the consulting engineers had the necessary skills and experience and were in an ideal position to carry out the role of planning supervisor.

Example

A power generating company required a major overhaul of a steam boiler. The generating company made an in-house appointment of its engineering works department as planning supervisor. This was because it wished to keep close control over the co-ordination and management of health and safety before tendering.

Example	*A client who had a multi-storey office block built under a design and build contract, appointed the design and build contractor as planning supervisor. The client decided under this form of procurement that the design and build contractor was the most relevant and competent organisation to act as planning supervisor.*
Example	*The client, a local authority, wanted the roof of a library to be replaced. The local authority made an in-house appointment and its property services department acted as planning supervisor. This was because the property services department had the competence and expertise for the job and an external appointment was felt unnecessary.*
Example	*A speculative developer who had very little knowledge of the construction process wanted four new town houses built. The developer appointed an architectural practice as the principal designer and planning supervisor for the project.*

Provide relevant information

26   The client has to provide the planning supervisor with information relevant to health and safety (CDM regulation 11). This includes information about the site, premises, work processes or activities where the construction work is to be carried out. The information may be to hand (eg existing drawings, plans showing the location of services or previous surveys of the land and structures). However, if it is not, the client needs to make reasonable enquiries to determine whether there is information which will be important to the designers when they are considering health and safety, and when the contractors carry out construction work. This might mean a survey of the site or premises will have to be carried out, and information obtained from public utilities or authorities (eg information on location of underground services). Typically, one of the designers or the planning supervisor might find this information on behalf of the client.

Example	*A client who owned and ran a warehouse needed substantial repairs to be carried out on the roof. Information about the roof, including the presence of fragile materials, access routes and the lack of edge protection was known by the client. This was passed to the planning supervisor for inclusion in the pre-tender stage health and safety plan.*

Example	*A factory owned by a client was closed and arrangements made for it to be demolished. The client had some information about the structure, the factory process and services supplying the factory. The client passed this information to the planning supervisor so it could be included in the pre-tender stage health and safety plan.*
Example	*A new road was to pass through land which had a history of industrial usage. There was no other option for the route. The client arranged for a site investigation of the route to be carried out. Information on the underground services, contamination, soil types and surrounding land uses, was obtained by a member of the design team. This was passed to the planning supervisor as well as to members of the design team who needed it.*
Example	*A chemical plant operator wanted two new storage tanks, associated pipework and pumping equipment to be installed at an existing plant. The client, who was also the planning supervisor, ensured information about underground services, risks from adjacent process plant and plant procedures was made available to the design team. Where appropriate, information was also included, in the pre-tender stage health and safety plan.*

27 Construction work may take place on premises which the client occupies, partially occupies or controls. The client, along with the planning supervisor and relevant designers, needs to consider the overlap of the construction work and the client's work activities to ensure the health and safety of employees, construction workers and others (eg members of the public). This could have a fundamental impact on how the construction work is carried out, what precautions might have to be adopted, and what information should go in the pre-tender stage health and safety plan. This will help the client to carry out their own legal duties as an employer under the HSW Act and the MHSW Regulations.

Example	*A local authority had to carry out extensive external maintenance work to a multi-storey occupied block of flats. The local authority provided extensive information about the premises to the planning supervisor. A work programme and procedures which minimised risks to the occupants was arranged for the project. Issues considered included means of access for members of the public, location of the site compound and hours of work.*

Example

The owner of an office block wanted to refurbish the building while it was still occupied by his employees. The project was planned to ensure that people who worked in the building and visitors were not put at risk by the construction work. Certain items of work were planned so that they were carried out at weekends when the building was empty.

Example

An oil company wanted some new plant to be built within an existing refinery complex. It fenced off the construction area and specified the access route from the main gate. It issued a blanket permit for works within the fenced area, but imposed its own permit-to-work procedure for all tie-ins.

THE PLANNING SUPERVISOR

The planning supervisor's key tasks during the concept and feasibility stage:
■ notification of the project to HSE
■ if requested, give advice to the client on the designers' competence and adequacy of provision for health and safety
■ ensure co-operation between designers
■ ensure as far as reasonably practicable that designers comply with their duties

Notification of the project

28   The planning supervisor should ensure that HSE is notified of the construction project if it is within the scope and application of the CDM Regulations and is notifiable - see paragraph 8 to 16 (CDM regulation 7). The notification should be sent to the local HSE office covering the site where construction work is to take place.

29   The notification can be made using Form 10 (rev). A copy of this is in Appendix 7. Other forms can be used so long as they contain the information laid down in Schedule 1 of the CDM Regulations. This is also in Appendix 7. The notification should be sent as soon as possible after the appointment of the planning supervisor. If some of the information needed to complete Form 10 (rev) is not available at the time it has to be sent, further details should be given to the local HSE office as soon as practicable after the appointment of the principal contractor.

Concept and feasibility

Advise the client

30 If requested, the planning supervisor should be in a position to give adequate advice to the client on:

(a) issues of competence; and

(b) the adequacy of the provision made for health and safety by any designer who the client arranges to prepare a design (CDM regulation 14(c)).

For further guidance on competence and provision for health and safety see Appendix 1.

Ensure co-operation between designers

31 The planning supervisor has to take reasonable steps to ensure co-operation between designers (CDM regulation 14(b)). This is so that the health and safety aspects of design are properly considered and co-ordinated, particularly where the work of different designers overlaps. To achieve this the planning supervisor needs to ensure so far as is reasonably practicable:

(a) that relevant information flows freely between the different designers (eg drawings);

(b) designers take proper account of health and safety in their design work and comply with their duties under CDM regulation 13; and

(c) designers co-ordinate their work to see how the different aspects of design interact with each other and affect health and safety.

32 The planning supervisor may need to contact designers to carry out points (a) to (c) in paragraph 31. Any conflict which could affect health and safety may need to be resolved. In some cases this might mean changing the design so that significant risks to health and safety are avoided.

Example

A safe system of work for the erection and installation of curtain walling can be affected by the design of the structural steel/concrete frame and the design of the curtain walling. Small changes to the frame design can make large differences to the safety of those installing certain types of curtain walling. The planning supervisor needs to ensure relevant information about the curtain walling design is passed to the frame designer and vice versa.

Ensure designers comply with their duties

33 The planning supervisor is under a duty (CDM regulation 14(a)) to ensure, so far as is reasonably practicable, that designers comply with their duties under CDM regulation 13. Depending on the nature and extent of the design work, the planning supervisor may need to carry out some form of review of designers' procedures. This will be to see how designers have analysed and assessed health and safety risks and tried to eliminate or reduce those remaining. This will probably mean looking at documented procedures on larger projects. On smaller projects a simple face to face questioning may be sufficient.

THE DESIGNER

The designer's key tasks during the concept and feasibility stage:
▩ make the client aware of their duties
▩ identify the significant health and safety hazards and risks of any design work
▩ give adequate regard to the hierarchy of risk control (see paragraphs 41 to 42)
▩ provide adequate information on health and safety to those who need it
▩ co-operate with the planning supervisor and, where appropriate, other designers involved in the project

34 Designers play a key role within the construction project in ensuring that the health and safety of those who are to construct, maintain or repair a structure are considered during the design process. Failure to do so could delay the project, make it much more difficult for contractors to devise safe systems of work and cause the client to make costly changes so that the structure can be maintained safely and efficiently.

35 As designs develop from initial concepts through to a detailed specification, different teams and individuals are involved. At each stage designers from all disciplines have a contribution to make in avoiding and combating health and safety risks inherent in the construction process and subsequent work. At different stages within the design process various mixes of design disciplines may be involved. For example, architects may produce a concept which is then developed in detail by a

Concept and feasibility

combined team from architectural and engineering backgrounds. The development of the detailed specification may then depend on a range of specialist teams. The most important contribution a designer can make to improve health and safety is often during the concept and feasibility stage. During this stage the designer's main considerations are about the different design options which are open so that potential hazards can be designed out.

Example	*The designer may be able to determine the location of the structure on the site. The location will affect how close construction plant has to come to railway lines, roads and overhead power lines.*

Example	*A bridge had to be built over an existing road which was a dual carriageway. The designer determined that with the maximum use of pre-fabricated bridge beams the extensive use of temporary works and resultant dangers could be avoided.*

36   When carrying out their duties under the CDM Regulations designers need to know to the extent that it is relevant to their role in the design process the following:

(a)   how hazards and risks to health and safety can arise in construction, maintenance and repair and how they can be avoided or reduced through design;

(b)   the methods used during construction, their sequence and possible overlapping nature;

(c)   the foreseeable maintenance and repair requirements of the structure being designed.

37   If such knowledge and understanding is not available in-house it may need to be brought into the designer's organisation, eg by consulting a health and safety specialist with experience of the design process. In some cases it may be appropriate to bring in construction expertise at an early stage. This often helps to overcome any separation between design considerations and construction methods. The interaction between specialists, those with construction expertise and designers should enable gaps in knowledge and understanding to be filled, particularly in the way design principles can be applied to avoid and reduce risk. Many clients already exploit construction expertise at an early stage when they carry out buildability, value engineering and whole lifetime costing exercises.

During these exercises care has to be taken not to jeopardise compliance with the CDM Regulations. However, the expertise gathered for these exercises can also be used to implement the principles of the CDM Regulations.

38　To help deal with the CDM Regulations in a structured way, designers may well find it useful to ensure that internal design office or where appropriate, quality assurance procedures, are appropriately altered or adapted. This will help ensure the requirements of the CDM Regulations are taken on board like other requirements of the design process. It will also help to make proper judgements when reaching design solutions which take due account of health and safety.

Make the client aware of their duties

39　If the client is unaware of their duties under the CDM Regulations, the designer should not begin preparing a design (CDM regulation 13(1)). Instead, the designer needs to explain these responsibilities to the client. Reference could be made to guidance published by HSC and HSE on the CDM Regulations (see page 76). Where appropriate, the designer could advise the client to seek professional advice and support to help them comply with the CDM Regulations.

Identify the significant health and safety hazards and risks of any design work

40　When designers carry out design work they have to consider the potential effect of their design on the health and safety of those carrying out construction work and others. This means the designer has to assess the risks of the design which can reasonably be foreseen (CDM regulation 13(3)). This usually includes risks to those building, maintaining, repairing or cleaning the structure and people who may be affected by such work.

41　To ensure that risks to health and safety are fully considered in the design process, designers will find it helpful to take the following steps:

(a)　identify the significant health and safety hazards likely to be associated with the design and how it may be constructed and maintained;

(b)　consider the risk from those hazards which arise as a result of the design being incorporated into the project under consideration;

(c)　if possible, alter the design to avoid the risk or where this is not reasonably practicable follow the remainder of the hierarchy of risk control (see paragraph 42);

Follow the hierarchy of risk control

42 When designing to reduce the risks, designers should apply the hierarchy of risk control. This consists of a series of steps which need to be taken when controlling risks:

(a) first consider if the hazard can be prevented from arising so that the risk can be avoided (ie alter the design to avoid the risk);

(b) if this cannot be achieved, the risk should be combated at source (eg ensure the design details of items to be lifted include attachment points for lifting);

(c) failing this, priority should be given to measures to control the risk that will protect all workers (eg allow a one-way system for delivery vehicles and spoil removal); and

(d) only as a last resort should measures be taken to control risk by means of personal protection.

43 The duties on designers when considering health and safety in their design work (CDM regulation 13(2)(a) and (b)) are qualified by what is reasonable for a designer to do at the time the design is prepared and by what is reasonably practicable. In determining what is reasonably practicable, the risk to health and safety produced by a feature of the design has to be weighed against the cost of excluding that feature by following the hierarchy of risk control.

44 The overall design process does not need to be dominated by a concern to avoid all risks during the construction phase and maintenance. However, a judgement has to be made by weighing up one consideration against another so the cost is counted not just in financial terms but also those of fitness for purpose, aesthetics, buildability or environmental impact. By applying these principles it may be possible to make decisions at the design stage which will avoid or reduce risks during construction work. In many cases, the large number of design considerations will allow a number of equally valid design solutions. What is important is that the approach to the solutions of design problems involves a proper exercise of judgement which takes account of health and safety issues.

Provide adequate information on health and safety to those who need it

45 If all factors have been considered, eg buildability, aesthetics etc and there are still risks which are not reasonably practicable to avoid, information needs to be given about the risks which remain. This

information needs to be included with the design to alert others to the risks which they cannot reasonably be expected to know. For further guidance on provision of information and co-operation, see paragraphs 53 to 56.

STAGE 2: DESIGN AND PLANNING

Design and planning

46   The key tasks of the client and the planning supervisor during the design and planning stages are the same as those in the concept and feasibility stage. However, the delivery of some of the tasks will vary in detail as the project develops. In addition the pre-tender stage health and safety plan needs to be prepared and a start made on the health and safety file. For details on the health and safety file see Appendix 4.

THE CLIENT

The client's key tasks during the design and planning stage:
▪ provide the planning supervisor and designers with information relevant to the health and safety of the project as this becomes available
▪ be reasonably satisfied that any designer(s) who the client arranges to prepare a design are competent and have made adequate provision for health and safety

THE PLANNING SUPERVISOR

The planning supervisor's key tasks during the design and planning stage:
▪ if requested, give advice to the client on the designer's competence and adequacy of provision for health and safety
▪ ensure designers continue to co-operate
▪ ensure designers comply with their duties
▪ ensure the pre-tender stage health and safety plan is prepared
▪ ensure the preparation of the health and safety file begins

Prepare the pre-tender stage health and safety plan

47   During this stage of the project, the planning supervisor should ensure that the pre-tender stage health and safety plan is prepared so that it is available for the tendering process, from which a principal contractor is selected (see paragraphs 57 to 63). If it is to be effective the planning supervisor and any other professional advisers responsible for putting together the tender documentation will need to determine what is the most suitable format of the pre-tender stage health and safety plan.

48 There are two main purposes of the pre-tender stage health and safety plan:

(a) First, it passes on information to the prospective principal contractors so that they can prepare outline submissions to it during tendering (see paragraph 60);

(b) Secondly, it allows the client (taking the advice of the planning supervisor or other professional advisers where appropriate) to assess the tender submissions of prospective principal contractors. For this second reason it is important to draw up the pre-tender stage health and safety plan so it requires specific answers to questions. There is little to be gained from merely outlining hazards or risks; details are needed on how the contractor will deal with them.

49 The level of detail, format and size of the pre-tender stage health and safety plan depends on a number of factors, including the nature of the project, the types of hazards and risks involved and the client's requirements. Appendix 2 outlines some of the issues which might be covered in the pre-tender stage health and safety plan, but each one is specific to each project.

Start to prepare the health and safety file

50 During the design and planning stage the preparation of the health and safety file needs to begin. The appropriate time will be determined by a number of factors including the planning supervisor's management and project procedures, the nature of the project, when the relevant design material is received and the client's needs. The preparation of the health and safety file is an on-going process up to the completion of the project (see paragraph 72 and Appendix 4).

THE DESIGNER

The designer's key tasks during the design and planning stage:
▪ identify the significant health and safety hazards and risks of the design
▪ give adequate regard to the hierarchy of risk control (see paragraphs 41 to 42)
▪ provide adequate information on health and safety to those who need it
▪ co-operate with the planning supervisor and where appropriate, other designers involved in the project

Design and planning

51 During this stage of a project the detailed design and specification work on the design options agreed during the concept and feasibility stage are carried out by designers. This may involve looking in closer detail at the work sections which make up the project. In this process designers can continue to make significant contributions to the avoidance and reduction of risks to health and safety.

Example

A designer considered using augured piles for a scheme to be built on contaminated land. However, he recognised that workers could be exposed to a toxic hazard. As a raft foundation was not viable from an engineering viewpoint, driven piles were specified. However, if augured piles had been the only reasonably practicable solution, the designer would have needed to include the possibility of exposure to toxic substances in information for the pre-tender stage health and safety plan.

Example

On a water treatment works a designer required a large number of manholes to give access to valves. He considered brick manholes, but specified for them to be be constructed from pre-cast concrete rings. Using the pre-cast rings minimised the amount of work required in the excavation and maximised the space available within the manhole for valve operation on completion of the project.

52 Designers who specify materials, substances, plant and equipment have to comply with CDM regulation 13. They should consider the hazards and risks which arise from using the products to be specified. Where reasonably practicable risks should be avoided or reduced by appropriate selection.

Example

The design of a party wall specified 100 mm blocks laid flat rather than 190 mm blocks. This avoided the need for repetitive handling of blocks weighing in excess of 20 kg. (This can still meet the requirements of the building regulations on noise transmission.)

Example

A duct work installer was overcome by fumes while applying a sealant to joints within a section of trunking. The designer had specified a solvent-based sealer. A water-based sealer with a similar performance was available.

| Example | *By specifying a 'non-fishtail' brick tie a designer eliminated the risk of cuts and eye injuries from temporarily exposed ties.* |

Provide adequate information on health and safety to those who need it

53   Designers have to provide adequate information on aspects of the design that might affect health and safety (CDM regulation 13(2)(b)). This information is essential to all parties who have to use the design information, eg the planning supervisor putting together the pre-tender stage health and safety plan and the health and safety file, the principal contractor and other contractors who use the design information and the actual individuals carrying out the work.

54   If basic design assumptions affect health or safety, or health and safety risks are not obvious from the standard design documents, the designer should provide additional information. This should include a broad indication of the designer's assumptions about the precautions needed for dealing with the risks. This information needs to be conveyed in a clear manner. The level of detail to be recorded should be determined by the nature of the hazards involved and the associated level of risk. This is a matter of professional judgement but the information could be included on drawings, in written specifications or outline method statements. If designers have suggested a particular or preferred working method to reduce risk, eg temporary support or a particular sequence of work to overcome temporary instability, the designer should make clear the principles of the design and describe any special requirements for the purposes of construction.

| Example | *A number of designers and contractors have been experimenting with developing existing drawings. This has a number of advantages, providing a means of passing on information in a user-friendly way from design to handover. The approach requires a drawing to be photo-reduced and then printed onto a standard (AO) size drawing. The 'border' can then be used to carry a range of additional information, eg pre-tender design information relevant to health and safety risks expected, 'as-built' materials, specifications, key maintenance details and periods, and key references to other documents. An example of a drawing prepared in this way is shown in the back of this publication.* |

| Example |

The design team responsible for a structural steel frame for a new stand at a stadium stipulated in a detailed specification the erection sequence of parts of the structure to avoid instability. Information was also provided about lifting points on certain steel members as well as identifying features of the structure which had a critical influence on its overall continuing stability and structural integrity during construction. The planning supervisor included this information in the pre-tender stage health and safety plan.

Co-operate with the planning supervisor and where appropriate, other designers involved in the project

55   Even on small projects it is unlikely that all the design work will be carried out by one designer. Designers therefore need to liaise with the planning supervisor and other designers so that they can co-ordinate their work to see how the different aspects of their designs interact with each other and affect health and safety. Liaison is also needed to enable the planning supervisor to ensure designers are fulfilling their duties (see paragraph 33).

56   If there is an overlap in the design work, there may be a need to exchange drawings and other design information which is relevant to health and safety. If a common format for the exchange of information is agreed within a project, this can help the process of co-operation. Agreement also needs to be reached to ensure health and safety is considered, eg agreeing acceptable access arrangements for services in ducts and above ceilings.

Design and planning

STAGE 3: TENDER/SELECTION STAGE

57 Principal contractor selection and appointment by the client is critical in determining the overall success of managing the construction phase. Health and safety are important aspects which need to be considered in this process. Pre-qualification procedures (see Appendix 1) and the use of the pre-tender stage health and safety plan are key means by which clients can be satisfied as well as they reasonably can that prospective principal contractors have made adequate provision for health and safety and are competent.

Time for tender process

58 To ensure health and safety is fully considered during the tendering process, the tender period should be long enough to allow prospective principal contractors to put their tender submissions together. If adequate time is given for the tender period and the tender documentation is structured appropriately, more attention can be paid to dealing with health and safety in tender submissions.

Tender documentation

59 Ideally, the tender documentation should be structured in a way that helps the decision making process of assessing whether prospective principal contractors have made adequate provision for health and safety and are competent. The documentation could therefore be structured to ensure a response by prospective principal contractors on health and safety against which judgements can be made. For example, detailed reference could be made to specific problems and how they will be controlled by the prospective principal contractors.

60 The pre-tender stage health and safety plan (see paragraphs 47 to 49 and Appendix 2) plays a vital role in the tender documentation. It enables prospective principal contractors to be fully aware of the project's health, safety and welfare requirements, particularly:

(a) the significant health and safety risks (especially those requiring specific resources);

(b) the standards to be applied to control the significant health and safety risks; and

(c) other specific details which might be laid down by the client (eg requirements for monitoring health and safety performance and project rules).

61 Clearly the way in which the pre-tender stage health and safety plan is included in the tender documentation and is structured is essential if responses are to be made by prospective principal contractors. A number of factors such as the nature of project, type of work activity and the requirements of the client will determine how the pre-tender stage health and safety plan is included in the tender documentation.

| Example |

On a small project where 15 three-bedroom houses were going to be built for a property developer, the architect and quantity surveyor put together the tender documentation. They decided the information in the pre-tender stage health and safety plan was more appropriately included in the bill of quantities, the specification and other tender documentation and not as a separate document. A covering note was sent with the tender documentation drawing attention to the relevant clauses.

| Example |

The tender documentation for a project which involved the construction of a 10 km foul water tunnel, associated pumping stations and sewer connections, was put together by the client's in-house professional advisers. They decided the pre-tender stage health and safety plan should be a stand-alone item in the tender documentation. This was highlighted in a covering letter to the tender documentation.

| Example |

Major health and safety issues dominated a project involving the replacement of process plant in a chemical works. The client decided the pre-tender stage health and safety plan needed to be very detailed as this was going to be the cornerstone of the tendering process. Parts of the tender documentation outlined what had to be done for health and safety and how it was to be done and called for specific items to be priced.

Prospective principal contractors

62 In response to the tender documentation prospective principal contractors could provide the following:

(a) their health and safety policy;

(b)   an outline submission giving evidence that health and safety has been adequately provided for in tender submissions in accordance with the pre-tender stage health and safety plan;

(c)   a clear specification of the resources to control and manage the major health and safety risks;

(d)   evidence of competence to carry out the construction work to the requirements of health and safety legislation.

Post tender

63   After tender submissions are received, the client (taking the advice of the planning supervisor or other professional advisers) needs to evaluate them. Further examination and discussion on the provision for health and safety and whether it has been adequately planned into the proposals for carrying out the construction work, could take place at post tender interviews. Any tenders which are significantly lower or have very short completion times could be investigated to find out why. If not enough detail on health and safety is included or the resources are underestimated the prospective principal contractor could be asked to explain why.

Tender/selection stage

STAGE 4: CONSTRUCTION PHASE

THE CLIENT

The client's key tasks during the construction phase:
■ ensure construction work does not begin until the principal contractor has prepared a suitable health and safety plan
■ comply with health and safety legislation where the client's work activities or undertaking may be affected by the construction work
■ be reasonably satisfied that any contractors who the client arranges to carry out construction work are competent and have made adequate provision for health and safety (eg 'nominated contractors')

Ensure the principal contractor's health and safety plan is suitable

64 The client has to ensure, so far as is reasonably practicable, that a suitable health and safety plan has been prepared by the principal contractor before construction work starts (CDM regulation 10). Enough time should be given for this task to be carried out.

65 The client is only expected to make a decision on whether the health and safety plan for the construction phase is suitable on the information which is available at the start of the construction phase. For many projects not all information relevant to the project may be available to develop the health and safety plan fully before the construction phase begins. For example, not all the design work may have been completed before the construction phase starts or many of the subcontractors who will be carrying out the work have yet to be appointed. This will particularly happen on projects involving various forms of management contracting and where design and build takes place. However, the health and safety plan should be sufficiently developed so that:

(a) the general framework for dealing with the management organisation, emergency procedures, arrangements for monitoring, communications, and welfare is in place; and

(b) it addresses the key tasks of the early work stages.

66 Clients may need to seek professional advice on whether the health and safety plan is suitable. Clients without in-house expertise, knowledge or skills could seek the advice of the planning supervisor, who if requested,

Construction phase

has a legal duty to provide this advice (CDM regulation 14(c)(ii)).

Client's work activities which may be affected by the construction work

67　If construction work takes place within premises or sites that are occupied, partially occupied or controlled by the client, agreement should be reached between the principal contractor and the client on issues such as division of responsibilities, co-ordination and areas of occupation. Much of this should be pre-arranged so that it is detailed in the pre-tender stage health and safety plan. However, this requires development in the principal contractor's health and safety plan so that both the client and the principal contractor know exactly what each has to do to comply with health and safety legislation. This may involve assessing various risks and agreeing appropriate control measures.

68　Throughout the construction work the client may need to monitor the interface of their work activities with the construction work. This ensures the proper discharge of legal duties as an employer (eg co-ordination and co-operation duties under the MHSW Regulations). The level of monitoring carried out will depend on the nature of the overlap, risks to employees and others.

> *Example*

A higher education college needed extensive external repairs to be carried out on a building which contained several lecture rooms, a canteen and staff rooms. The pre-tender stage health and safety plan included details about the selection of plant to keep noise levels down, the degree of overhead protection, the numbers and location of means of escape in case of fire to be kept clear, the time of day when scaffolding could be erected, etc. When the principal contractor was appointed the college agreed various further items to ensure the safety of students, college staff and visitors. These included the phasing of works, monitoring and liaison arrangements and site security.

> *Example*

A chemical company appointed a principal contractor to replace roof sheets above pressure vessels containing highly flammable materials. The chemical company had responsibilities towards the contractor's workers, which involved laying down specific rules, and giving a thorough briefing on emergency procedures, as well as providing information about access to the roof. This was all detailed in the pre-tender stage health and safety plan. After the principal contractor was appointed, both he and the client developed these issues further in the health and safety plan for the construction phase.

Example

A water authority appointed a civil engineering contractor to enlarge a sewage works while normal operation continued. The water authority included in the pre-tender stage health and safety plan information on the sewage works, rules and emergency procedures. After appointing the principal contractor this information was included in the health and safety plan for the construction phase along with agreed liaison and co-ordination procedures. In addition detailed arrangements were agreed between all parties for the commissioning and handover of installed plant.

THE PLANNING SUPERVISOR

The planning supervisor's key tasks during the construction phase:
■ if requested, advise the client on the principal contractor's health and safety plan
■ ensure designers comply with their duties and co-operate
■ continue to prepare the health and safety file

Advise the client on the health and safety plan

69   If the client requests, the planning supervisor should be in a position to give adequate advice on the suitability of the health and safety plan prepared by the principal contractor before construction work begins - see paragraphs 64 to 66, (CDM regulation 14(c)(ii)).

Ensure designers comply with their duties and co-operate

70   If design work is carried out during the construction phase, the planning supervisor should ensure so far as is reasonably practicable that designers comply with their duties and co-operate (CDM regulation 14(a) and (b)). Typical design work carried out during the construction phase is listed in paragraph 73.

71   The guidance outlined in paragraphs 31 to 33 on the planning supervisor during the earlier stages of a construction project also applies to the construction phase. In addition, arrangements may be needed to ensure there is adequate liaison and communication between the planning supervisor, principal contractor and the organisation(s) carrying out the design. This will allow the relevant parties to comply with their legal duties by ensuring that design information is shared between the

appropriate people and significant design variations are dealt with in a structured manner.

Continue to prepare the health and safety file

72   As the construction phase proceeds, further information relevant for inclusion in the health and safety file becomes available. This may come from the design work of specialist subcontractors and the 'as built' drawings produced after alterations are made by contractors following variations. Individual contractors should give this information to the principal contractor who then passes it on to the planning supervisor. Ideally, this is carried out as a continual process as the information becomes available and should not be left until the project has been completed.

THE DESIGNER

The designer's key tasks during the construction phase:
▦ identify the significant health and safety hazards and risks of ongoing design work, eg temporary works, variations and further elements of detailed design
▦ give adequate regard to the hierarchy of risk control (see paragraphs 41 to 42)
▦ provide adequate information on health and safety to those who need it
▦ co-operate with the planning supervisor and, where appropriate, other designers involved in the project

73   If design work is carried out during the construction phase, whoever is responsible for it is under a duty to comply with CDM regulation 13. This design work may include:

(a)   temporary works design (eg falsework and designed scaffolds);

(b)   specialist subcontractors carrying out design (eg mechanical and electrical contractors);

(c)   significant design variations (eg at the request of contractors or due to unforeseen circumstances).

The principles of designing for health and safety during the construction phase are the same as those for earlier stages of a project. Paragraphs 40 to 45 and 52 to 56 give guidance on these principles.

Construction phase

Example

At a water treatment works large diameter sections of steel pipe were welded internally, involving confined space working with associated health risks (welding fumes) and safety risks (electric shock because of a totally conducting environment). The work required a watchman to oversee the job at all times. The contractor carried out a design variation to the pipe jointing arrangement so that external welding was possible. This saved the cost of the watchman and of the pre-testing of the atmosphere within the pipe before entry. In the first instance the designer responsible for the pipework joints could have avoided the risks.

Example

Extensive repair work needed to be carried out on the stonework of the facade of a building which had a shop at ground floor level. At first floor level along the facade a permanent concrete canopy cantilevered out over the pavement. A heavy duty scaffold was required for the work to the upper storeys of the front because of the nature of the work.

From information provided by the client and included in the health and safety plan, it was clear that the canopy was inadequate to support such a scaffold. A two-storey suspended scaffold was therefore designed which was built down from the roof level. The designer of the scaffold also had to allow for the raising and lowering of materials and for access to the facade of the building to enable the work to be carried out.

THE PRINCIPAL CONTRACTOR

The principal contractor's key tasks during the construction phase:
▪ develop and implement the health and safety plan
▪ be reasonably satisfied that when arranging for a contractor to carry out construction work, they are competent and have made adequate provision for health and safety
▪ obtain and check safety method statements from contractors
▪ ensure the co-ordination and co-operation of contractors (particularly under the MHSW Regulations and the Provision and Use of Work Equipment Regulations 1992[5])

■ ensure training for health and safety is carried out

■ have appropriate communication arrangements between contractors on site for health and safety

■ make arrangements for discussing health and safety matters with people on site

■ allow only authorised people onto site

■ display notification details

■ monitor health and safety performance

■ pass information to the planning supervisor for the health and safety file

The health and safety plan

74   Before construction work starts the principal contractor should ensure that the pre-tender stage health and safety plan (see paragraphs 47 to 49 and Appendix 2) is developed. It should become a specific document which sets out the arrangements for securing the health and safety of all those who are carrying out the construction work and all others who may be affected by it. The client should ensure so far as is reasonably practicable that it is satisfactory (see paragraphs 64 to 66).

75   Not all information relating to the project may be available to develop the health and safety plan fully before construction work begins. However, site layout drawings covering the project at different stages, completed design information, and the pre-tender stage health and safety plan are valuable in developing the health and safety plan so that:

(a)   the general framework is in place (including arrangements for welfare);

(b)   it deals with the key tasks during the initial stages and work packages where design is complete.

76   The principal contractor's organisation and arrangements for managing health and safety should include procedures for ensuring health and safety is considered in construction phase planning. This might involve setting up a team to prepare the health and safety plan and build on the work carried out at the tendering stage when evidence of competence and resources to address the health and safety needs of the project were demonstrated to the client and planning supervisor (see paragraph 62).

Construction phase

The nature and complexity of the project will determine the size of the team. For example, on a larger project the senior member of the principal contractor's project team, including those directly involved in managing the project, could be involved. Where appropriate other expertise, particularly in health and safety, may be included. On a small project it may be appropriate for the person who is in control of the site to prepare the health and safety plan. Appendix 3 outlines the suggested contents of the health and safety plan for the construction phase. This might be a useful guide to direct the work of the team.

77 When developing the health and safety plan, the principal contractor needs to identify the hazards and assess the risks at each of the main stages within the construction phase. To do this properly, information, including safety method statements, may be needed from the contractors who will be working at the site, (see paragraphs 82 to 83). If risks arise because a number of contractors are exposed to a common hazard (eg from site transportation or from the site electrical distribution system), the principal contractor needs to take a positive role in ensuring the risks are controlled and managed.

78 The health and safety plan needs to be kept up to date, modified and altered in the light of changing circumstances and standards achieved on site and as the construction work progresses. Safety method statements and information from contractors starting during the different work stages of a project will invariably mean parts of the health and safety plan have to be amended and updated. Reviews of parts of the health and safety plan may also need to be made if there are design changes or alterations, unforeseen circumstances or variations to planned circumstances arise. It is vital that such changes are notified to all parties working on site who will be affected.

Select and appoint contractors (including specialist contractors)

79 If the principal contractor puts together tender documentation for the various contractor packages of the project, prospective contractors need to be given information about the project, the site and relevant parts of the health and safety plan, including where appropriate:

(a) the arrangements for the health and safety management of the construction work;

(b) references to recognised codes of practice and HSC and HSE publications relevant to the risks of the work to be carried out;

(c) the monitoring arrangements;

(d) site rules and procedures, eg wearing personal protective equipment, training or competence requirements;

(e) the rules for further subcontracting work.

80   The specific requirements for health and safety need to be made very clear. This will give prospective contractors enough information to ensure that provision is made for health and safety in their tender submission. The tender documentation could be structured in a way to ensure a response by prospective contractors on health and safety against which judgements can be made. This will help the principal contractor to determine the resource and competence requirements for the particular package of work and whether the prospective contractors have addressed these issues.

81   After prospective contractors have submitted their tenders the principal contractor may usefully hold a post tender interview. At the interview the contractor's attitude and competence to health and safety can be judged. This can be done by asking, for example, why they have either excluded or included health and safety items in their tender bid, how they intend to meet their legal duties, whether they will further subcontract work and how this work will be controlled.

Obtain and vet safety method statements

82   If a contractor is to carry out work which has risks to health and safety, a safety method statement on how they intend to control and manage these risks may need to be prepared. The contractor should base the safety method statement on assessment of the risks to the health and safety of their employees and others (see Appendix 5). To help, the principal contractor can fully brief the contractor about anticipated construction methods, site or design factors, and the relevant parts of the health and safety plan for the construction phase. The principal contractor needs to check the safety method statement to ensure:

(a) all the risks to health and safety have been assessed;

(b) adequate health and safety arrangements have been specified;

(c) it is compatible with the health and safety plan;

(d) it is compatible with the work or proposed work of other contractors.

83   Once the safety method statement has been agreed the principal contractor needs to consider the nature and timing of the work, and

where necessary ensure that the activity of one contractor's work will not create additional risks for another. When the contractor starts work on site the principal contractor needs to monitor whether the safety method statement is being followed and implemented as agreed.

<table><tr><td>Example</td></tr></table>

The principal contractor for a project involving the building of a six-storey office block arranged for the drylining subcontractor to work in the stairwells over week-ends. This avoided the staircases being blocked by workers, access platforms and materials during the week when large numbers of people were working on site.

Ensure co-ordination and co-operation of contractors

84 The principal contractor needs to make sure that there is an integrated approach to health and safety on site which assists contractors (including the self-employed) to comply with specific legal requirements. Ensuring co-ordination and co-operation between contractors is an on-going task throughout the project which should be addressed and reviewed at project or site meetings and includes the following:

(a) emergency arrangements and procedures (eg fire, including means of escape and first aid provision);

(b) provision and use of plant and equipment which will be used by a number of contractors (eg cranes and hoists);

(c) co-ordinating the work of contractors so that the activity of one contractor will not create a risk for another;

(d) ensuring contractors receive relevant health and safety information.

85 If plant, equipment and welfare facilities are shared by a number of contractors, the principal contractor should co-ordinate its provision, use and maintenance. Details regarding control, co-ordination and management of shared equipment such as scaffolding and lifting equipment could be specified in the health and safety plan by the principal contractor.

Ensure training for health and safety is carried out

86 The levels of competence in health and safety and the corresponding basic training standards which are acceptable for the construction work could be made clear in the health and safety plan developed by the

principal contractor. Some of these may have been specified by the planning supervisor in the pre-tender stage health and safety plan. This allows contractors who intend to work on site to determine the training, experience and competence requirements of the people they propose to employ to carry out the work.

87 There are many established training standards for people who carry out tasks such as fork-lift truck driving, scaffolding and first aid. These include the certification schemes for plant operators, scaffolders, demolition operatives and first aid qualifications approved by HSE. If people do not meet these standards, or a similar or equivalent standard, it could be made clear that they will not be allowed to work on the site until they have been adequately trained and are able to carry out the job properly, without risks to health and safety.

88 The principal contractor is responsible for ensuring all newcomers to the site are given site awareness training regardless of their position or experience in the construction industry. The training could give details of the main hazards, organisational arrangements, the health and safety management system for the site, emergency and evacuation procedures and specific site rules. Ideally, no newcomers should be allowed to start work on site unless they have undergone site awareness training, even on the smallest sites. This training may be followed up with an on-going health and safety awareness programme.

89 On-going training could take the form of toolbox or task health and safety talks where contractors discuss health and safety issues with their employees. The talks should be specific, practical and relevant to the current operations. Toolbox or task health and safety talks could be made a contractual requirement or form part of the rules of the health and safety plan. The effectiveness of site awareness and on-going training is enhanced greatly by the active participation of senior project managers and supervisors. Safety method statements could form the agenda for toolbox or task health and safety talks.

Have appropriate communication arrangements between contractors on site for health and safety

90 Good and effective communications between all parties are essential if common understanding and agreement is to be established on managing health and safety. This is vital, especially if the health and safety plan is to be understood and consistently implemented.

91 The arrangements for communications could be spelt out in detail in the health and safety plan (see Appendix 3, part 2). This includes matters such as the frequency of project or site meetings and how health and safety is to be dealt with at these meetings.

92 At project or site meetings health and safety should be high on the agenda and not be passed over at the end of the meeting due to lack of time. Each project meeting needs to consider health and safety performance. Past performance may be reviewed by considering how well the health and safety plan has been implemented. Active monitoring (see paragraph 105) and any preventive measures arising out of investigated accidents and incidents could be reviewed by the principal contractor.

93 At project or site meetings poorly performing contractors could be identified and action to improve matters agreed. This then needs to be followed up. The contractors' representatives should be given enough time to air their problems about meeting planned procedures. Contractors also need to be informed of modifications to the health and safety plan.

94 When significant variations to design or planned procedures are necessary, enough time should be allowed to ensure appropriate precautions are devised. The review of past performance can mean that the lessons learnt are applied to the rest of the project.

The following matters could be included on the agenda at project or site meetings:

- recommendations and action taken or outstanding, following regular active monitoring by site management and, where appropriate, health and safety advisers

- reports of accidents, dangerous occurrences, near misses and complaints, including analysis and follow-up action

- recommendations of any safety committee

- pre-planning in the light of project progress and work which has to be done before the next project meeting, including updating the health and safety plan

- inter-relationship of contractors' work to ensure co-ordination and co-operation, especially with respect to project progress

Make arrangements for discussing health and safety matters with people on site

95 The principal contractor has to make sure that:

(a) people on site can discuss and offer advice on health and safety; and

(b)   there are arrangements for the co-ordination of the views of people on site.

Ideally these arrangements will be detailed in the health and safety plan. They should allow employees and the self-employed to discuss and offer advice on matters which affect their health and safety during the construction phase. The detail of these will vary depending on the size, nature and complexity of the project, number of people on site and whether recognised trade unions have appointed safety representatives.

96   The Safety Representatives and Safety Committee Regulations 1977[6] detail the cases in which recognised trade unions may appoint safety representatives, specify the function of such representatives, and set out the obligations of employers towards them. If safety representatives are appointed, their employers should provide them with the facilities and assistance necessary to carry out their functions which include inspection, investigation, representation and consultation on behalf of the workers they represent.

97   If a safety committee is requested by safety representatives and it happens to be a site-wide committee, the principal contractor could use it as a forum for discussing and co-ordinating the views of people on site. However, if the safety committee is not site-wide and only relates to part of the work activities on site, the principal contractor has to consider alternative arrangements for co-ordinating people's views on site.

98   If a site does not have any safety representatives, it may be useful for the principal contractor to set up a safety committee. It could play a major role in scrutinising health and safety arrangements and reviewing overall performance as well as providing a forum for people on site to discuss and offer advice. Matters raised in safety committee meetings could be referred to project or site meetings. Action notes from both meetings could be given to both the relevant workers and site management to check whether or not instructions are carried out. Similar action is needed for health and safety inspection reports and whenever decisions need to be taken on preventive action, for example after an accident investigation.

99   On smaller sites it may not be appropriate to set up a safety committee, however the principal contractor still needs to make some arrangements to allow anyone working on site to discuss and offer advice on health and safety.

Example

The principal contractor on a project involving the construction of six units on an industrial estate arranged for the site agent to be the point of contact for discussing and taking views on health and safety from those working on site. The principal contractor put up posters in the site welfare facilities informing the people on site of these arrangements.

Example

On a project involving the construction of a large office block, the principal contractor set up a safety committee so that workers could discuss or offer advice on health and safety. The committee had representatives of the workforce on site. The terms of reference and arrangements for the operation of the safety committee were set down in the health and safety plan.

Example

On a large civil engineering project a continuing improvement programme was developed. As part of this programme there were regular discussions with site workers. This consisted of a monthly meeting with sections of the workforce in rotation. The meeting took about two hours, and was run by the project manager and other section supervisors. Employees were encouraged to raise both positive and negative matters, and any items raised by operatives which could be achieved were dealt with. Not only was there an improvement in health and safety performance, but also in productivity.

Allow only authorised people onto site

100　The principal contractor should take reasonable steps to ensure that only authorised people are allowed into any area where construction work is taking place (CDM regulation 16(1)(c)).

A list of typical authorised people:

■　contractors or employees carrying out construction work

■　those who need to enter the work area for purposes connected with the work, (eg architects, engineers and representatives of the client)

■　individuals or organisations who have a statutory right to enter the work area (eg HSE inspectors and building control inspectors)

101 To ensure that only authorised people enter the work area the principal contractor may need to set up an 'authorisation' procedure. On a large and complex project a 'pass' scheme could be established so that only those who have a pass are allowed onto the site. A pre-requisite requirement for authorisation (or obtaining a pass) could be enforced, eg everyone could be given site awareness training before they start work on site (see paragraph 88). On smaller projects it may only be necessary for people to report to the site agent or supervisor to gain authorisation.

102 The principal contractor has to determine the most appropriate exclusion methods to prevent those not authorised from entering the site. This should be based upon the nature of the project and where it is located. Some of the reasonably practicable steps which principal contractors can take to exclude people from the work area are described in HSE Guidance Note GS 7 *Accidents to children on construction sites*[7]. If the site is within the client's premises the exclusion methods need to be agreed with the client (see paragraphs 67 to 68).

Display notification details

103 A copy of the notice which the planning supervisor has to ensure is sent to the local HSE office (see paragraphs 28 to 29) should be clearly displayed on site by the principal contractor. The notice should be in a position where it can be easily read by people working on the site, eg on the entrance gate to the site, or in site huts.

104 The principal contractor should inform all contractors who work on site about the contents of the notice. The information it contains could be given to contractors in tender documentation or once they have been appointed to the project.

Monitor health and safety performance

105 Monitoring health and safety performance is a site management function. Health and safety specialists can act as advisers in this process. The arrangements for monitoring should be detailed in the health and safety plan (see Appendix 3, part 2). Monitoring has two components:

(a) **Active monitoring** which provides feedback to the principal contractor and other contractors, and where appropriate, to the client and planning supervisor on standards that are being achieved. It is designed to pick up the circumstances liable to lead to an accident or ill health. The main purpose is to measure success in achieving standards, not to highlight failure. It can be used to recognise and reward good compliance with standards. Active inspection of plant, processes and procedures is essential. This

Construction phase

includes statutory inspections, eg of excavations, scaffolding or lifting tackle as well as consideration of the safe systems of work, safety method statements, permits-to-work and other systems. A checklist can be helpful to ensure a systematic inspection is carried out. The inspection system should have a way of checking that remedial action is taken and monitored by senior management.

(b) **Reactive monitoring** which concentrates on accidents, incidents and ill health. It tends to highlight weaknesses in standards achieved. Investigation needs to be carried out by competent people, and to a depth appropriate to the severity or the potential severity of the outcome. Investigation systems are needed to respond reliably to and analyse sub-standard performance. Investigation is a line management responsibility but specialist advice may be needed.

106 The principal contractor and other contractors should use the data from active and reactive monitoring to take preventive or remedial action to improve performance in the future. This information could also be used at project reviews (see paragraphs 126 to 128).

107 To be effective a monitoring system should have a quality check built into it on how well line management is carrying out the monitoring function. Senior managers should check, for example, the extent to which agreed site inspection standards are being followed. It also shows how much management is committed to controlling risks and caring for the health and safety of the workforce. Monitoring the safety performance of managers and supervisors shows them that health and safety is important. Further guidance on monitoring is available in HSE's publication HS(G)65 *Successful health and safety management*[8].

Pass information to the planning supervisor for the health and safety file

108 Any information which the principal contractor possesses which needs to be included in the health and safety file should be passed to the planning supervisor. This is ideally carried out as a continual process as the information becomes available. The principal contractor may find it helpful to discuss the health and safety file with the planning supervisor. This helps determine what information the planning supervisor requires, how it is to be recorded and the arrangements for passing it to the planning supervisor. The principal contractor also needs to obtain any relevant information which subcontractors might have and pass it to the planning supervisor. Further guidance on the health and safety file can be found in Appendix 4.

CONTRACTORS

<table>
<tr><td colspan="1">Contractors' key tasks during the construction phase:</td></tr>
<tr><td>identify the hazards of their work, assess the risks arising from these hazards and tell the principal contractor how these risks are to be controlled</td></tr>
<tr><td>inform the principal contractor of any death, injury, ill health or dangerous occurrence</td></tr>
<tr><td>provide the principal contractor with information to be included in the health and safety file</td></tr>
<tr><td>co-operate with the principal contractor and other contractors</td></tr>
<tr><td>comply with the rules in the health and safety plan</td></tr>
<tr><td>follow any directions of the principal contractor so that the latter can comply with duties under the CDM Regulations</td></tr>
<tr><td>provide information to employees</td></tr>
</table>

109 Contractors' duties under the CDM Regulations are essentially in support of those on the principal contractor. As well as these duties, contractors still have responsibility for the health and safety of their own employees and others affected by their work under existing health and safety legislation, eg HSW Act, MHSW Regulations and regulations dealing specifically with construction health and safety. Detailed guidance for small contractors is given in HSE's publication *Health and safety for small construction sites*[9].

Identify hazards, assess the risks, and provide information to the principal contractor

110 Contractors need to identify the hazards of their work activities on site and assess the risks which result from this work. The principal contractor needs to be informed of these risks, particularly how they are to be controlled, managed and where they affect others (eg members of the public, other contractors and employees of the client). This information may need to be outlined in a safety method statement (see Appendix 5). The information is essential to the principal contractor to develop and amend the health and safety plan where necessary and ensure co-ordination of the work activities on site.

111 Contractors may also have to consult the principal contractor about the risks arising from the work of other contractors and where necessary incorporate precautions against these risks in any safety method statements which they prepare.

Construction phase

112 Contractors should promptly inform the principal contractor of any death, injury, ill health or dangerous occurrence as defined in the Reporting of Injuries, Diseases and Dangerous Occurrences Regulations 1985[10] (CDM regulation 19(1)(e)). This allows time for the principal contractor to investigate the circumstances of any accident or dangerous occurrence, consider if adequate precautions were in place and if changes to the health and safety plan are required.

113 Any information which should be included in the health and safety file (see Appendix 4) and is in the possession of contractors needs to be passed to the principal contractor (CDM regulation 19(f)(ii)). This could include information about the plant and equipment installed and 'as built' drawings.

Co-operate with the principal contractor and other contractors

114 Contractors should co-operate with the principal contractor and other contractors so that all can comply with their legal duties (CDM regulation 19(1)(a)). This might include providing safety method statements to the principal contractor when requested so that procedures can be agreed before work starts, and work is scheduled to fit in with other contractors. It also means attending project or site meetings.

Comply with rules in the health and safety plan and directions of the principal contractor

115 Any rules which the principal contractor makes will be written in the health and safety plan (CDM regulation 16(3)). Ideally these will be brought to the contractor's attention through the tendering or selection process and at regular project or site meetings. The rules have to be complied with by contractors and if appropriate also by employees working for contractors, the self-employed, and visitors. The rules could cover issues such as further subcontracting work, monitoring of health and safety performance, wearing personal protective equipment and permit-to-work arrangements.

116 The principal contractor may give directions to contractors so that they can comply with duties under the CDM Regulations (CDM regulation 16(2)(a)). Contractors should comply with these directions which may involve issues such as procedures for authorising people to work on site and requesting evidence to ensure contractors have provided employees with information about health and safety.

Provide information to employees

117 Before employees start work on a construction site contractors should inform them of:

(a) the names of the planning supervisor and principal contractor; and

---

(b) information from the health and safety plan which is relevant to their employees (eg emergency arrangements, rules and health and safety risks from other contractors' work).

---

118 On some sites this information might be given to employees by the principal contractor with site awareness training (see paragraph 88). If this is not the case contractors need arrangements to communicate this information to employees. On larger sites this could be done in writing. On smaller sites it could be carried out verbally.

The self-employed

119 The term 'self-employed' is defined in the HSW Act 1974 as "... an individual who works for gain or reward otherwise than under a contract of employment, whether or not he himself employs others". Many people working on construction sites hold tax certificates which describe them as self-employed. However, there are a number of factors which determine whether or not an individual is genuinely self-employed or whether it is for tax purposes only. These factors include the degree of control exercised over the work, the ability to further subcontract and the question of who provides tools and equipment for the work. If a person is self-employed for tax purposes only, they may still be considered as an employee as far as health and safety legislation is concerned. It may in practice be advisable for the principal contractor or contractors to treat them as one of their own employees, as far as health, safety and welfare issues are concerned. They will then be subject to the same duties as any other employee.

120 The genuinely self-employed are responsible for their own health and safety and that of others affected by their work. If they are themselves contracted to carry out operations, their responsibilities are the same as for any other contractor, and they should co-operate with other contractors on the site. If they have control of another person's activities they should ensure that these people are not put at risk.

STAGE 5: COMMISSIONING AND HANDOVER

121 The tasks which have to be carried out in the construction phase continue into the commissioning and handover stage. For some projects the commissioning and handover stage may be as long as the construction phase itself. In some cases it might be a separate project or it could involve a new principal contractor. Considerable health and safety risks can arise both during commissioning and 'snagging' work before handover. These need to be identified, assessed and suitable precautions taken, eg new means of access and escape, safe working places and permit-to-work systems may need to be provided. New health risks, often caused by substances and materials used in process plant, also have to be considered.

122 The principal contractor needs to review the health and safety plan so that additional or altered arrangements are incorporated and risks that arise during commissioning are controlled. Where appropriate this task needs to be carried out in conjunction with the relevant designers, contractors and the client. When reviewing the health and safety plan, responsibilities between the different parties involved need to be defined and lines of communication made clear. This is particularly important where commissioning work is taking place in occupied premises or where a number of contractors are involved. Co-ordination between the principal contractor and the client is of paramount importance, especially for phased handovers and joint commissioning arrangements. In such scenarios there should be a focal point (person) who is identified and nominated to deal with health and safety co-ordination throughout the commissioning and handover stage.

123 Establishing a schedule of tests and a programme for carrying out the commissioning work helps to review the health and safety plan. This determines what work has to be carried out, by whom and when. It highlights if there are any concurrent operations which could create additional risks, who is responsible for what and the risks which have to be managed. This may result in detailing new emergency and monitoring procedures in the health and safety plan and making permits-to-work part of the site rules.

124 Enough time needs to be allowed for the commissioning stage to be completed safely. This is essential where complex mechanical, electrical and computer systems are involved or clients have set crucial deadlines.

125 Information which is required for the health and safety file needs to be forwarded to the planning supervisor. This usually includes operational and maintenance manuals for plant and equipment and 'as installed' drawings (for further details on the health and safety file, see Appendix 4).

PROJECT REVIEW

126 Feedback from the experience of a construction project is important so that clients, designers, planning supervisors, principal contractors and contractors can evaluate the adequacy of existing health and safety management systems and procedures and adapt them to future projects. Learning from experience through project reviews enables organisations to develop and maintain their ability to manage risks more reliably and to a greater extent.

127 Reviews are ideally conducted by different levels of management throughout the life of a project. They can be based on information from active and reactive monitoring. Managers should judge whether performance is good enough, recognise success, decide on the need for improvements and when to apply them to solve problems.

128 At present feedback on health and safety does not often occur systematically within the construction industry and experience from specific projects is rarely reviewed. If any formal review does happen it tends to concentrate almost exclusively on cost and profit implications rather than include health and safety management. HSE studies[11] have shown that there are opportunities to save costs using a health and safety management system which uses suitable standards to focus on risk control. Project reviews should look at a number of issues which provide an overview for senior managers.

Issues which could be included in project reviews:

- the relevance and appropriateness of the standards set in the health and safety plan and how they could be improved;

- assessment of the degree of compliance with standards and the implementation of remedial action;

- identification of areas where standards were absent;

- accident, ill health and incident data, accompanied by analysis of both the immediate and underlying causes, trends and common features and remedial action taken;

APPENDIX 1

COMPETENCE AND PROVISION FOR HEALTH AND SAFETY

Appendix 1

1 CDM regulations 8 and 9 contain legal requirements on competence and provision for health and safety. Duties are placed on:

■ the client when appointing a planning supervisor
■ any person when arranging for a designer to prepare a design or a contractor to carry out or manage construction work

Under the CDM Regulations a person is a corporate entity or individual, who carries out any of the duties under the Regulations. This therefore means more than just a client arranging for a designer or a contractor to carry out work; it includes a designer arranging for another designer to carry out design work or a contractor arranging for another contractor to carry out or manage construction work.

Competence and provision for health and safety

2 Competence has to be considered in the light of the health and safety duties which will fall to the prospective duty holder. This does not only cover the general issues of the duty holder's organisation and arrangements for managing health and safety. It should also be related to the specific aspects of the project under consideration and the range of differently skilled individuals working within the organisation whose experience can be brought to bear on the project. Competence is not merely a matter of technical qualifications or training achievements, although these may be important. It is a wider assessment of abilities relevant to the work to be carried out.

3 Provision for health and safety means the allocation of adequate resources for the purposes of carrying out duties under the CDM Regulations and complying with health and safety legislation. Resources include people with the appropriate training and skills to carry out the required duties, equipment, technical facilities, and sufficient time to carry out legal duties. Where appropriate the following areas of work should be considered:

■ planning and design
■ preparation of health and safety plans
■ selection of designers and contractors
■ sequencing and scheduling of the work
■ carrying out the construction work or parts of it
■ preparation of the health and safety file

4 The specialist competencies needed within the project can only be determined within that project, but a set of questions will be needed which relates to these special details. There may also be a need to include questions about key people who are allocated to the project in terms of their experience and knowledge of the particular health and safety issues and their level of awareness and training.

Assessment of competence and provision for health and safety

5   The actual assessment process may be quite detailed on large or complex projects, but it can be a very simple one on small works, or those involving low risks. The level of questioning and detail required will depend upon the risks involved in the work and the nature of the construction project. The assessment of competence is crucial to selection and appointment; but it does need to be proportionate and appropriate. The process needs to seek clear answers to well structured questions. It may require additional documentary proof, but there is little point in merely collecting documents; they should fulfil a clear purpose in the assessment process.

6   As part of pre-qualification procedures over the past few years, certain supporting documents have regularly been required during the selection process. However, before asking for any documentation you need to ask yourself what questions you hope it will answer, and have a clear method for assessing the contents.When looking at documents which show historic trends and performance, for example accident information and enforcement records, you need to be aware that this can paint a distorted picture, and may not be a good indicator of current competence. Analysis of documentation may itself need specialist help and advice.

7   The list below outlines some of the more common documents which you could ask for:

- company health and safety documents (including risk assessment and safety method statement procedures)
- accident and ill health records
- records of previous enforcement action
- training records (including relevant continuing professional development)
- quality assurance procedures
- project review and monitoring documents

The fact that an organisation cannot provide some or even all of these documents may not mean they are lacking competence or suitable resources. However, you will have to look in some detail to establish why they cannot. On the other hand, avoid being swayed by just lengthy or glossy brochures; there is no guarantee the organisation follows the procedures or even that it wrote the documents.

8   How far this process is followed on smaller contracts is a matter for individual duty holders. It may be that the types of questions and supporting documentary evidence can be compressed into a few minutes' discussion for a small piece of work. However, some competency assessment does need to be done and seen to be carried out.

9   Pre-qualification and selection are already established procedures within the industry. In many cases this is carried out as a two-stage process. The first stage (pre-qualification) is carried out in general terms, sufficient to judge whether an organisation should be included on the list of those invited to tender for a specific project or to be listed on an approved tender list. The second stage involves organisations who were selected during the first stage, going through a more rigorous second assessment based on their submissions to tender documentation.

10   When carrying out pre-qualification procedures the industry already uses question schedules. These may be tied into consideration of supporting documents or may stand alone. However, some form of assessment is carried out. In paragraphs 12 to 16 in this appendix, a number of key areas have been outlined with some useful questions to ask. This is not meant as an exhaustive list, but it should help duty holders, particularly those undertaking competency assessment for the first time.

11   The pre-tender stage health and safety plan can be used as a key document in the process of tender assessment for provision for health and safety during the selection of a principal contractor. It will raise specific issues that prospective principal contractors will be expected to provide answers to in their outline tender submissions. Considering these answers will help in making a judgement as to whether prospective principal contractors have adequate provision for health and safety and in determining competence. The same principles can be applied when selecting other contractors to work on the project.

Some of the key areas to probe

12   In the following sets of questions, some of the more common areas to consider are outlined. Not every project will need all the areas to be covered. Also, not every duty holder will be able to answer all the questions. However, they do provide a basis for assessment. If prospective duty holders can answer all these questions well then they are likely to be able to demonstrate a better performance. Understanding the answers will not be easy in every case, and as with documentation assessment you may need to seek specialist help. Although the questions have been written as if the person answering

is an organisation, the same approach can be applied to a sole trader.

General policy

13   These areas are about the way the duty holder sets out their policy for health and safety:

- How does the organisation's management demonstrate an understanding of their legal duties with respect to health and safety?
- Are there clear processes and procedures within the organisation to carry out risk assessment? How are the results of such assessments turned into effective means of reducing or controlling risk? How are these procedures monitored?
- Is there a clear understanding within the organisation about how accidents and ill health arise in the construction process?
- How does the organisation keep up to date with developments in health and safety?

General organisation

14   These questions consider the way the duty holder organises for health and safety matters:

- What arrangements are in place to advise on health and safety matters? Are 'in-house' experts or external consultants relied upon? How is health and safety advice integrated into the organisation's procedures?
- How are the capabilities and expertise of employees assessed and those of any organisation subcontracted to carry out work?
- What sort of health and safety training does the organisation carry out for its staff?
- How does the organisation ensure that information on health and safety is passed on to its staff?

Planning and monitoring

15   This section covers the way in which the duty holder plans and monitors aspects of their performance and activities relevant to health and safety:

- What procedures does the organisation have for managing information relevant to health and safety? How are changes which are notified during the development of a project dealt with?
- How does the organisation monitor performance on health and safety matters, and how does it take corrective action? Does it carry out systematic reviews on health and safety performance?

Appendix 1

■ How does the organisation demonstrate its ability to manage people and processes which will be relevant to health and safety within the project?

Specialist knowledge, abilities, resources and experience

16 In this section questions on special areas which are relevant to specific aspects of the project are asked:

■ What specialist back-up and technical facilities does the prospective organisation have which will be relevant to the project?

■ What is the organisation track record on comparable activities?

General points

17 If requested, the planning supervisor should be in a position to give adequate advice to the client on issues of competence and provision for health and safety. This applies when the client arranges for a designer to prepare a design or arranges for a contractor to carry out or manage construction work (CDM regulation 14(c)). Clients with a limited knowledge of the construction process or the issues of competence and provision for health and safety are strongly recommended to take advice from the planning supervisor.

18 Neither the client nor other duty holders need to carry out further checks to ensure that there is a continuing level of competence, nor to check that resources are actually expended in the way that was initially planned. However, if a client or other duty holder chooses to monitor whether resources are being used in the way they were intended to be allocated and a continuing level of competence is being maintained, the health and safety standards tend to be higher than average and significant quality and cost benefits can be achieved.

APPENDIX 2

THE PRE-TENDER STAGE HEALTH AND SAFETY PLAN

This appendix helps you to consider the matters which could be included in the pre-tender stage health and safety plan. Some of the items may not be relevant to your project. The level of detail should be determined by the health and safety risks of the project. Projects involving minimal risks call for simple straightforward pre-tender stage health and safety plans. Large projects or those involving significant risks will require more detail.

Guidance on preparing the pre-tender stage health and safety plan and its use in the tendering process can be found in paragraphs 47 to 49 and 59 to 61.

Possible information for inclusion in the pre-tender stage health and safety plan

1   *Nature of the project*

- Name of client.
- Location.
- Nature of construction work to be carried out.
- Timescale for completion of the construction work.

2   *The existing environment*

- Surrounding land uses and related restrictions, eg premises (schools, shops or factories) adjacent to proposed construction site, planning restrictions which might affect health and safety.
- Existing services, eg underground and overhead lines.
- Existing traffic systems and restrictions, eg access for fire appliances, times of delivery, ease of delivery and parking.
- Existing structures, eg special health problems from materials in existing structures which are being demolished or refurbished, any fragile materials which require special safety precautions, or instability problems.
- Ground conditions, eg contamination, gross instability, possible subsidence, old mine workings, or underground obstructions.

3   *Existing drawings*

- Available drawings of structure(s) to be demolished or incorporated in the proposed structure(s) (this may include a health and safety file prepared for the structure(s) and held by the client).

4   *The design*

- Significant hazards or work sequences identified by designers which cannot be avoided or designed out and, where appropriate, a broad indication of the precautions assumed for dealing with them.

- The principles of the structural design and any precautions that might be needed or sequences of assembly that need to be followed during construction.
- Detailed reference to specific problems where contractors will be required to explain their proposals for managing these problems.

5 *Construction materials*

- Health hazards arising from construction materials where particular precautions are required, either because of their nature or the manner of their intended use. These will have been identified by designers as hazards which cannot be avoided or designed out. They should be specified as far as is necessary to ensure reliable performance by a competent contractor who may be assumed to know the precautionary information that suppliers are, by law, required to provide.

6 *Site-wide elements*

- Positioning of site access and egress points (eg for deliveries and emergencies).
- Location of temporary site accommodation.
- Location of unloading, layout and storage areas.
- Traffic/pedestrian routes.

7 *Overlap with client's undertaking*

- Consideration of the health and safety issues which arise when the project is to be located in premises occupied or partly occupied by the client.

8 *Site rules*

- Specific site rules which the client or the planning supervisor may wish to lay down as a result of points 2 to 7 or for other reasons, eg specific permit-to-work rules, emergency procedures.

9 *Continuing liaison*

- Procedures for considering the health and safety implications of design elements of the principal contractor's and other contractors' packages.
- Procedures for dealing with unforeseen eventualities during project execution resulting in substantial design change and which might affect resources.

SUGGESTED CONTENTS OF THE HEALTH AND SAFETY PLAN DURING THE CONSTRUCTION PHASE

This appendix helps you to consider the matters which could be included in the health and safety plan for the construction phase. Some of the items may not be relevant to your project. The level of detail should be determined by the health and safety risks of the project. Projects involving minimal risks call for simple straightforward plans. Large projects or those involving significant risks will require more detail.

Guidance on preparing the health and safety plan for the construction phase can be found in paragraphs 74 to 78.

What should the health and safety plan start with?

1   The health and safety plan can usefully open with:

■   a description of the project; and

■   a general statement of health and safety principles and objectives for the project;

■   information about restrictions which may affect the work, (eg neighbouring buildings, utility services, vehicular and pedestrian traffic flows and restrictions from the work activities of the client).

What arrangements should be set out in the health and safety plan for managing and organising the project?

2   These can include:

Management

■   the management structure and responsibilities of the various members of the project team whether based at site or elsewhere.
■   arrangements for the principal contractor to give directions and to co-ordinate other contractors.

Setting standards

■   the health and safety standards to which the project will be carried out. These may be set in terms of statutory requirements or higher standards which the client may require in particular circumstances.

Information for contractors

■ means for informing contractors about risks to their health and safety arising from the environment in which the project is to be carried out and the construction work itself.

Selection procedures

■ the principal contractor's arrangements for ensuring that all:

  ☐ contractors, the self-employed and designers to be appointed by the principal contractor are competent and will make adequate provision for health and safety;

  ☐ suppliers of materials to the principal contractor will provide adequate health and safety information to support their products;

  ☐ machinery and other plant supplied for common use will be properly selected, used and maintained; and that operator training has been provided.

Communications and co-operation

■ means for communicating and passing information to all members of the project team, including the client and any client's representatives, designers, the planning supervisor, the principal contractor, other contractors, site workers and others whose health and safety may be affected.

■ arrangements for securing co-operation between contractors for health and safety purposes.

■ arrangements for management meetings and initiatives by which the health and safety objectives of the project are to be achieved.

■ arrangements for dealing with design work carried out during the construction phase, ensuring it complies with CDM regulation 13 and resultant information is passed to the appropriate person(s).

Activities with risks to health and safety

■ arrangements for the identification and effective management of activities with risks to health and safety, by carrying out risk assessments, incorporating those prepared by other contractors, and also safety method statements which result. These activities may be specific to a particular trade (eg falsework) or to site-wide issues, and may include:

  ☐ the storage and distribution of materials;

  ☐ the movement of vehicles on site, particularly as this affects pedestrian and vehicular safety;

  ☐ control and disposal of waste;

- the provision and use of common means of access and places of work;
- the provision and use of mechanical plant which is used by a number of contractors;
- the provision and use of temporary services, eg electricity;
- temporary support structures, eg falsework;
- commissioning, including the use of permit-to-work systems;
- protection from falling materials;
- exclusion of unauthorised people.

Control measures to deal with these should be clearly set out, including protection of members of the public.

Emergency procedures

- emergency arrangements for dealing with and minimising the effects of injuries, fire and other dangerous occurrences.

Reporting of RIDDOR information

- arrangements for informing the principal contractor about accidents, ill health and dangerous occurrences which need to be notified to HSE under the Reporting of Injuries, Diseases and Dangerous Occurrences Regulations 1985.

Welfare

- the arrangements for the provision and maintenance of welfare facilities.

Information and training for people on site

- arrangements by which the principal contractor will check that people on site have been provided with:
  - health and safety information;
  - health and safety training; and
  - information about the project (the names of the planning supervisor and principal contractor and relevant parts of the health and safety plan) by their employer:
    - arrangements for project specific awareness training;
    - arrangements for toolbox or task health and safety talks;
    - arrangements for the display of statutory notices.

Consultation with people on site

- arrangements that have been made for consulting and co-ordinating the views of people on site or their representatives.

Appendix 3

Site rules

◼ arrangements for making site rules and for bringing them to the attention of those affected. The rules should be set out in the health and safety plan. There may be separate rules for contractors, site workers, visitors and other specific groups.

Health and safety file

◼ arrangements for passing on information for the preparation of the health and safety file.

Arrangements for monitoring

◼ arrangements should be set out for active and reactive monitoring to achieve compliance with:
  ☐ legal requirements; and
  ☐ the health and safety rules developed by the principal contractor through regular planned checks, and by carrying out investigations of incidents (whether causing injury, loss, or 'near miss') and complaints. This may involve:
    ○ co-operation and regular meetings between senior management and those who provide health and safety advice to them.
◼ monitoring of:
  ☐ procedures, eg contractor selection and the management of certain trades;
  ☐ on-site standards actually achieved compared with those set for the project.

Project review

◼ reviews throughout the project, as different trades complete their work and at its conclusion. This means that the lessons learnt in terms of the standards set and those actually achieved can be taken forward.

APPENDIX 4   THE HEALTH AND SAFETY FILE

1   The health and safety file is a record of information for the end user
which focuses on health and safety. The information it contains will alert
those who are responsible for the structure and equipment in it of the
significant health and safety risks that will need to be dealt with during
subsequent use, construction, maintenance and cleaning work.

2   The planning supervisor has to ensure that the health and safety file is
prepared. To carry out this task it helps if procedures are set up for
obtaining and collating the information to be included in the health and
safety file. These procedures may need to detail what information is to be
collected, how it is to be collected, presented and stored. They could be
part of the planning supervisor's arrangements for dealing with health
and safety or part of quality assurance systems. On larger projects it may
be necessary to include details relating to the health and safety file in the
pre-tender stage health and safety plan to ensure an ordered delivery of
information.

Relevant information which could be included in the health and safety file

- ■ 'record' or 'as built' drawings and plans used and produced
  throughout the construction process;
- ■ the design criteria;
- ■ general details of the construction methods and materials used;
- ■ details of the equipment and maintenance facilities within the
  structure;
- ■ maintenance procedures and requirements for the structure;
- ■ manuals produced by specialist contractors and suppliers which
  outline operating and maintenance procedures and schedules for
  plant and equipment installed as part of the structure; and
- ■ details of the location and nature of utilities and services, including
  emergency and fire-fighting systems.

3   The planning supervisor may find it useful to discuss the health and
safety file with the client. This helps determine what information the
client requires and how the client wishes the information to be stored
and recorded.

4   Designers and the principal contractor need to ensure so far as is
reasonably practicable that any features of the structure which will
involve significant risk to health and safety during the structure's lifetime
are passed to the planning supervisor. The principal contractor also
needs to obtain details of services, plant and equipment which are part of
the structure from specialist supply and installation contractors, eg
mechanical and electrical contractors and pass this information on.

5   Much of the material for the health and safety file comes from the information which designers are required to provide under CDM regulation 13(2)(b) (see paragraphs 53 to 54). Providing this information on drawings allows it to be amended if any variations arise during construction. It also allows health and safety information to be stored on the same document (see paragraphs 12 to 16 in this appendix).

6   On completion of the project the planning supervisor has to hand over the health and safety file to the client. In some cases it might not be possible for a fully developed health and safety file to be handed over at the end of the project. This may happen because the construction work had to be finished rapidly to meet a tight deadline and completion of the health and safety file was impossible. Clearly a common sense approach may be needed, allowing the health and safety file to be handed over as soon as practical after a completion certificate or similar document has been issued. What is important is that work on producing the file continues throughout the project and is not left until the end.

7   The health and safety file should be kept available for inspection by the client and ideally on the premises to which it relates. It may be useful to store the health and safety file so that it is in two parts. One part will be more relevant for day to day use, eg operational and maintenance manuals. The other part is for longer term use, eg drawings which will only be required when major alteration work is carried out. The health and safety file could, if the client wishes, be stored electronically. It could also be stored on microfiche. In whatever form it is stored, it should be easily accessible.

8   For ease of reference it may be useful for the planning supervisor to produce a document which summarises the key elements of the health and safety file and acts as a quick guide to where the relevant information is stored.

9   When construction work is going to be carried out on a structure for which the client possesses a health and safety file, the client should pass it to the planning supervisor. This forms part of the relevant information which has to be made available. The planning supervisor will then in turn need to ensure that the designers are given the relevant information from the health and safety file. Moreover, relevant parts of the health and safety file may need to be incorporated into the pre-tender stage health and safety plan. Once this construction work has been completed, the health and safety file or parts of it will need to be amended and updated.

10   On a project which involves work on part of a structure for which there is no health and safety file, a health and safety file only has to be created in relation to the construction work carried out and not for the whole of the structure. Eventually as further work is carried out on that structure the health and safety file will be added to and amended, allowing an

increasingly detailed file to be developed.

11   For projects which involve the building of domestic houses by a developer, each property needs a health and safety file. The infrastructure associated with the development (eg roads and sewers) will also require a health and safety file. Relevant information will need to be passed to the local authority and utility companies.

Drawings

12   The provision of 'as built' and 'as installed' drawings is a common requirement in most contracts. Drawings are a good vehicle for the transmission of information between designer, contractor and back to the client. Drawings can also be a very good way of providing information required under the CDM Regulations, particularly for inclusion in health and safety plans and the health and safety file.

13   The accuracy and usefulness of 'as built' and 'as installed' drawings varies in common experience. While absolute accuracy may not always be possible, attempting to achieve this will improve the provision of information. There can be difficulties in gathering all the information needed for accurate 'as built' and 'as installed' drawings. On large projects it may be necessary to set up clear procedures to collect and validate this data. There may be many ways of presenting and storing this information. This is likely to develop over the coming years.

14   A number of designers and contractors have been developing approaches to 'as built' and 'as installed' drawings and two examples are produced at the back of this publication.

15   In the first drawing, some temporary site huts with the mechanical and electrical services all marked are reproduced. This was prepared for a health and safety file as the huts were to be handed to another contractor. A notes section for maintenance and demolition is included on the drawings.

16   In the second drawing a tender drawing for a cut and cover tunnel has been surrounded by detailed 'as built' information in the drawing margin. Again, there are sections for maintenance and demolition. This was prepared for a health and safety file and is self-explanatory.

Appendix 4

APPENDIX 5

PRINCIPLES OF RISK ASSESSMENT AND THE PRODUCTION OF A SAFETY METHOD STATEMENT

1   Risk assessment is the evaluation of risks which may arise from hazards at work. The objective is to identify the measures needed to eliminate, or if not possible, to minimise the risks.

2   Risk assessment has to be carried out by law, under the MHSW Regulations, and applies generally to all work activities. There are also requirements for risk assessment under other regulations dealing with specific hazards, eg the Control of Substances Hazardous to Health Regulations 1994[12], the Manual Handling Operations Regulations 1992[13] and the Personal Protective Equipment Regulations 1992[14]. Assessments made under the other regulations will meet in part the general requirement and so do not have to be repeated under the MHSW Regulations. However, it is important to ensure that all significant hazards are covered.

3   A risk assessment comes from a structured approach to the work in question in the light of experience, the sequence of operations to be followed, the known hazards associated with each phase and existing legal requirements. Each stage should be thought through properly, precautions planned and implemented accordingly. The detail needed in the risk assessment depends on the nature of the risk.

4   If the work is sufficiently similar to other jobs which have been assessed for risks, a fresh assessment may not be needed. The original assessment could be modified to suit the new circumstances.

5   Although not required by law, preparing a written safety method statement after carrying out a risk assessment has proved to be an effective way of producing an action plan. It also secures the objective of the assessment to identify the necessary health and safety measures. It is particularly useful in bringing together the assessments of the various hazards which might arise in any particular job. This means a single comprehensive safety method statement could take account of all the assessments.

6   In many cases, safety method statements could be closely linked with, or even form part of a company's safety policy and procedures. However, there may be cases where the company's safety policy and procedures do not cover the particular circumstances of the work, eg use of piling rigs next to live motorways, work next to or over a fast flowing river, or work on contaminated land. In such cases the particular circumstances and their associated risks must be assessed.

Appendix 5

7   The safety method statement could also form part of the health and safety plan after it has been agreed with the principal contractor.

8   The procedure for carrying out a risk assessment and producing a safety method statement can be as illustrated below:

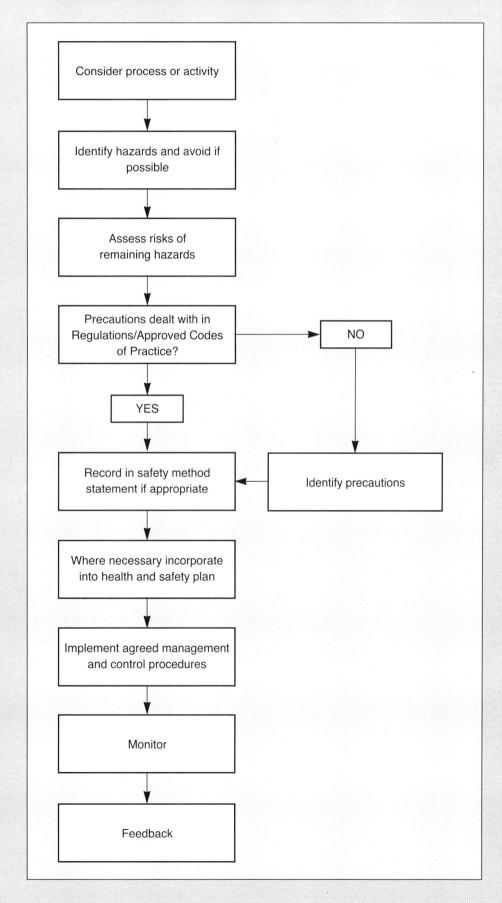

Appendix 6

APPENDIX 6 — REQUIREMENTS OF THE CDM REGULATIONS AT THE MAIN STAGES OF A CONSTRUCTION PROJECT

	CONCEPT AND FEASIBILITY	DESIGN AND PLANNING	TENDER/SELECTION STAGE	CONSTRUCTION PHASE	COMMISSIONING AND HANDOVER
CLIENT	Appoint planning supervisor (regulation 6(1)(a))		Appoint principal contractor (regulation 6(1)(b))		
	Planning supervisor to be competent and have made adequate provision for health and safety (regulations 8(1) and 9(1))		Principal contractor to be competent and have made adequate provision for health and safety (regulations 8(3) and 9(3))	Ensure that when arranging for any contractor(s) to carry out or manage construction work, they are competent and have made adequate provision for health and safety (regulations 8(3) and 9(3))	
	Provide planning supervisor with relevant information (regulation 11)			Comply with health and safety legislation where client's work activities overlap with the construction work (HSW Act, MHSW Regs, etc).	
	Ensure that when arranging for any designer(s) to prepare a design, they are competent and have made adequate provision for health and safety (regulations 8(2) and 9(2))			Ensure so far as is reasonably practicable, that the principal contractor's health and safety plan is suitable (regulation 10)	Take such steps as is reasonable for the client to take to keep health and safety file available for inspection (regulation 12(1))
	Ensure notification is submitted to HSE (regulations 7(1) and 7(3))		Ensure further notification details which were not known at the time of appointment are sent to HSE (regulation 7(4))		

PLANNING SUPERVISOR

If required, be in a position to give adequate advice to client on competence and provision for health and safety by designers (regulation 14(c)(i))

Ensure, so far as reasonably practicable, designers comply with duties (regulation 14(a))

Take such steps as is reasonable for the planning supervisor to take to ensure co-operation between designers (regulation 14(b))

...be in a position to give adequate advice to check on competence and provision for health and safety a)

contractors
(regulation 14(c)(ii))

If required, be in a position to give adequate advice to contractors on competence and provision for health and safety by designers
(regulation 14(c)(i))

If required give adequate advice to client on the suitability of the health and safety plan prepared by principal contractor
(regulation 14(c)(ii))

Deliver health and safety file to client
(regulation 14(f))

Ensure pre-tender stage health and safety plan is prepared
(regulation 15(1) - (3))

Ensure health and safety file is prepared
(regulation 14(d))

Where appropriate, take reasonable steps to inform the client of their duties under the CDM Regulations
(regulation 13(1))

Give adequate regard to the hierarchy of risk control when carrying out design work
(regulation 13(2)(a))

Ensure design includes adequate information about health and safety
(regulation 13(2)(b))

Co-operate with the planning supervisor and other designers
(regulation 13(2)(c))

Ensure that when arranging for any designer(s) to prepare a design they are competent and have made adequate provision for health and safety
(regulations 8(2) and 9(2))

Ensure that when arranging for any contractor(s) to carry out or manage construction work, they are competent and have made adequate provision for health and safety
(regulations 8(3) and 9(3))

UPERVISOR

DESIGNERS

Appendix 6

REQUIREMENTS OF THE CDM REGULATIONS AT THE MAIN STAGES OF A CONSTRUCTION PROJECT *(continued)*

CONCEPT AND FEASIBILITY	DESIGN AND PLANNING	TENDER/SELECTION STAGE	CONSTRUCTION PHASE	COMMISSIONING AND HANDOVER
			Ensure health and safety plan is prepared for construction work and is kept up to date (regulation 15(4))	
			Take reasonable steps to ensure co-operation between contractors (regulation 16(1)(a))	
			Ensure compliance with rules if these are made, take reasonable steps that only authorised people are allowed onto site and display notification form (regulation 16(1)(b) - (d))	
			Provide planning supervisor with information relevant to the health and safety file (regulation 16(1)(e))	
			May give directions to contractors (regulation 16(2)(a))	
			May make rules in the health and safety plan. If they are made, they should be in writing (regulations 16(2)(b) and (3))	
			So far as is reasonably practicable, ensure information is provided to contractors (regulation 17(1))	
			So far as is reasonably practicable, ensure contractors provide training and information to employees (regulation 17(2))	
			Ensure discussions with and advice from people at work and that there are arrangements for the co-ordination of views from people on site (regulation 18)	

PRINCIPAL CONTRACTOR

Ensure that when arranging for any designer(s) to prepare a design they are competent and have made adequate provision for health and safety (regulations 8(2) and 9(2))

Ensure that when arranging for any contractor(s) to carry out or manage construction work they are competent and have made adequate provision for health and safety
(regulations 8(3) and 9(3))

Co-operate with principal contractor
(regulation 19(1))

Pass to principal contractor information which will affect health and safety, is relevant to the health and safety file or is relevant to RIDDOR
(regulations 19(b), (e) and (f))

Comply with directions of principal contractor and rules in health and safety plan
(regulations 19(c) and (d))

Provide information and training to employees
(HSW Act, MHSW Regulations, etc)

Ensure that when arranging for any designer(s) to prepare a design they are competent and have made adequate provision for health and safety
(regulations 8(2) and 9(2))

Ensure that when arranging for any contractors to carry out or manage construction work they are competent and have made adequate provision for health and safety
(regulations 8(3) and 9(3))

CONTRACTORS

HSE
Health & Safety Executive

Notification of project

Note

1. This form can be used to notify any project covered by the Construction (Design and Management) Regulations 1994 which will last longer than 30 days or 500 person days. It can also be used to provide additional details that were not available at the time of initial notification of such projects. (Any day on which construction work is carried out (including holidays and weekends) should be counted, even if the work on that day is of short duration. A person day is one individual, including supervisors and specialists, carrying out construction work for one normal working shift.)

2. The form should be completed and sent to the HSE area office covering the site where construction work is to take place. You should send it as soon as possible after the planning supervisor is appointed to the project.

3. The form can be used by contractors working for domestic clients. In this case only parts 4-8 and 11 need to be filled in.

HSE - For official use only

Client	V	PV	NV	Planning supervisor	V	PV	NV
Focus serial number				Principal contractor	V	PV	NV

1   Is this the initial notification of this project or are you providing additional information that was not previously available

Initial notification ☐   Additional notification ☐

2 Client: name, full address, postcode and telephone number *(if more than one client, please attach details on separate sheet)*

Name: Telephone number:
Address:
Postcode:

3 Planning Supervisor: name, full address, postcode and telephone number

Name: Telephone number:
Address:
Postcode:

4 Principal Contractor *(or contractor when project for a domestic client)* name, full address, postcode and telephone number

Name: Telephone number:
Address:
Postcode:

5 Address of site: where construction work is to be carried out

Address:
Postcode

F10 (rev 03.95)

6 Local Authority: name of the local government district council or island council within whose district the operations are to be carried out

>

7 Please give your estimates on the following: Please indicate if these estimates are original ☐ revised ☐ *(tick relevant box)*

a. The planned date for the commencement of the construction work

b. How long the construction work is expected to take *(in weeks)*

c. The maximum number of people carrying out construction work on site at any one time

d. The number of contractors expected to work on site

8 Construction work: give brief details of the type of construction work that will be carried out

>

9 Contractors: name, full address and postcode of those who have been chosen to work on the project *(if required continue on a separate sheet) .(Note this information is only required when it is known at the time notification is first made to HSE. An update is not required)*

>

Declaration of planning supervisor

10 I hereby declare that .... *(name of organisation)* has been appointed as planning supervisor for the project

Signed by or on behalf of the organisation .... *(print name)* ....

Date ....

Declaration of principal contractor

11 I hereby declare that .... *(name of principal contractor)* has been appointed as principal contractor for the project. *(or contractor undertaking project for domestic client)*

Signed by or on behalf of the organisation .... *(print name)* ....

Date ....

Schedule 1 of the Construction (Design and Management) Regulations 1994

Particulars to be notified to the Executive

1 Date of forwarding.

2 Exact address of the construction site.

3 Name and address of the client or clients, (see note).

4 Type of project.

5 Name and address of the planning supervisor.

6 A declaration signed by or on behalf of the planning supervisor that he has been appointed as such.

7 Name and address of the principal contractor.

8 A declaration signed by or on behalf of the principal contractor that he has been appointed as such.

9 Date planned for start of the construction phase.

10 Planned duration of the construction phase.

11 Estimated maximum number of the people at work on the construction site.

12 Planned number of contractors on the construction site.

13 Name and address of any contractor or contractors already chosen.

Note: When a declaration has been made in accordance with regulation 4(4), item 3 above refers to the client or clients on the basis that that declaration has not yet taken effect.

GLOSSARY

These definitions will help readers to understand the way in which terms are used in this guidance.

Cleaning work: This is the cleaning of any window or any transparent or translucent wall, ceiling or roof in or on a structure, where such cleaning involves a risk of a person falling more than 2 metres.

Client: Clients are those who are involved in a trade, business or other undertaking (whether for profit or not) and for whom construction work is carried out.

Construction work: The carrying out of any building, civil engineering or engineering construction work and includes any of the following:

- the construction, alteration, conversion, fitting out, commissioning, renovation, repair, upkeep, redecoration or other maintenance (including cleaning which involves the use of water or an abrasive at high pressure or the use of substances classified as corrosive or toxic for the purposes of regulation 7 of the Chemicals (Hazard Information and Packaging) Regulations 1993, de-commissioning, demolition or dismantling of a structure;
- the preparation for an intended structure, including site clearance, exploration, investigation (but not site survey) and excavation, and laying or installing the foundations of the structure;
- the assembly of prefabricated elements to form a structure or the disassembly of prefabricated elements which, immediately before such disassembly, formed a structure;
- the removal of a structure or part of a structure or of any product or waste resulting from demolition or dismantling of a structure or from disassembly or prefabricated elements which, immediately before such disassembly, formed a structure; and
- the installation, commissioning, maintenance, repair or removal or mechanical, electrical, gas, compressed air, hydraulic, telecommunications, computer or similar services which are normally fixed within or to a structure;

but does not include the exploration for or extraction of mineral resources or activities preparatory thereto carried out at a place where such exploration or extraction is carried out.

Contractor: Contractors include subcontractors and may also be known as works, specialist trade or nominated contractors. They have health and safety responsibilities for their own employees and others.

Design: Design is a wide term and includes specification and the production of drawings, design details and bills of quantity.

Designers: Designers are the organisations or individuals who carry out the design of the project. Designers may include architects, consulting engineers, quantity surveyors, specifiers, principal contractors and specialist subcontractors.

Hazard: Something with the potential to cause harm.

Health and safety file: This is a record of information for the client which focuses on health and safety. It alerts those who are responsible for the structure and equipment in it of the significant health and safety risks that will need to be dealt with during subsequent use, construction, maintenance, repair and cleaning work.

Health and safety plan: The health and safety plan serves two purposes. The pre-tender stage health and safety plan prepared before the tendering process brings together the health and safety information obtained from the client and designers and aids selection of the principal contractor. The health and safety plan during the construction phase details how the construction work will be managed to ensure health and safety.

Monitoring: Monitoring has two components:

■ *active*. This measures performance against plans and standards that have been worked out and agreed at the start of the contract. It shows how much management is committed to achieving objectives and maintaining standards;

■ *reactive*. This involves the investigation of accidents and incidents, and the analysis of data from specific investigations.

Notifiable: Construction work is notifiable if it lasts longer than 30 days or will involve more than 500 person days of work.

Planning supervisor: The planning supervisor is a company, partnership, organisation or an individual who co-ordinates and manages the health and safety aspects of design. The planning supervisor also has to ensure that the pre-tender stage of the health and safety plan and the health and safety file are prepared.

Principal contractor: This is the contractor appointed by the client who has the overall responsibility for the management of site operations. This includes the overall co-ordination of site health and safety management.

Project: This means a project which includes or is intended to include construction work.

Glossary